the Forth Naturalist and Historian

Volume 37 2014

1-3 Prelims
4 Author Addresses

Naturalist Papers

5 Dunblane Weather Report 2013 – Neil Bielby
17 Changes in the King's Park Flora during the last Hundred Years – Roy Sexton
31 Rookeries in the Upper Forth Bird Recording Area – Neil Bielby
43 2012 and 2013 Moth Records For Stirlingshire and West Perthshire – John T. Knowler
49 Forth Area Bird Report 2013 – Chris Pendlebury
77 Report on the Forth Naturalist and Historian Wildlife and Landscape Forum 2013 – Michael Usher

Historical Papers

83 Upper Carron Valley and the Highland Drovers – John Mitchell
87 Loch Lomondside's Heraldic Birds and Beasts – John Mitchell
91 Prehistoric Pottery from Excavations at the Smith Art Gallery and Museum Stirling – Nick Aitchison

The Changing Biodiversity of Central Scotland

101 Man and the Landscape Conference 2013 – Richard Tipping
107 What Factors have had the most Impact on Central Scotland's Biodiversity during the last 30 years – Stirling Scottish Wildlife Trust

What's Changed Surveys 1983 – 2013

111 Giant Hogweed in the River Allan and the Upper Forth – Guy Harewood
121 Tailend Moss - a 30 Year Investigation of the Aquatic Invertebrate Fauna – Craig Macadam
129 A Survey of the Hoverflies of the Inner Forth – Scott Shanks
135 Falkirk Moths – Heather Young
139 A Survey of Large Heath, Purple Hairstreak and Northern Brown Argus Butterfly Populations in the Forth Valley – Stuart Bence and Lorna Blackmore

Published by the Forth Naturalist and Historian, University of Stirling – charity SCO 13270.

ISSN 0309-7560

ISBN 978-1-898008-72-9

Cover: front– Rainfall anomaly map of the UK December 2013 – supplied by the Met Office.

Printed by Meigle Colour Printers Ltd., Tweedbank Industrial Estate, Galashiels.
Set in Zapf Calligraphic on 115 gsm Silk and cover 300 gsm Silk.

THE FORTH NATURALIST AND HISTORIAN

The Forth Naturalist and Historian (FNH) is an informal enterprise of Stirling University. It was set up in 1975 by several University and Central Regional Council staff to provide a focus for interests, activities and publications of environmental, heritage and historical studies for the Forth area, comprising now local authority areas Stirling, Falkirk and Clackmannanshire.

Since then the organisation of an annual environment/heritage symposium called *Man and the Landscape* has been an important feature.

The annual *Forth Naturalist and Historian* has published numerous papers, many being authoritative and significant in their field, and includes annual reports of the weather, and of birds in the locality, plus book reviews and notes. These volumes provide a valuable successor to that basic resource *The Transactions of the Stirling Field and Archaeological Society*, 1878-1939. Four year contents/indexes are available, and selected papers are published in pamphlet form, while others are available as reprints.

In addition a 230 page book *Central Scotland – Land, Wildlife, People,* a natural history and heritage survey, was produced in 1994 and is available in the form of a CD-Rom, *Heart of Scotland's Environment* (HSE).

Other FNH and associated publications still in print include – *Mines and Minerals of the Ochils*, *Airthrey and Bridge of Allan*, *Woollen Mills of the Hillfoots*, *The Ochil Hills* – landscape, wildlife, heritage – an introduction with walks, *Alloa Tower and the Erskines of Mar*, and the *Lure of Loch Lomond* a journey round the shores and islands. Several of these are in association with Clackmannanshire Field Studies Society.

FNH publications are listed on the internet British Library (BLPC) and by booksellers e.g. Amazon, Bol, Barnes and Noble.

Offers of papers/notes for publication, and of presentations for symposia are ever welcome. **Visit website for instructions to authors.**

Honorary Secretary Marilyn Scott,
Computer Services, University of Stirling, FK9 4LA.
E-mail: fnh@stir.ac.uk
Web: http://www.fnh.stir.ac.uk

Author Addresses

Nick Aitchison, 22a Snowdon Place, Stirling FK8 2JN

Stuart Bence, 14 Stein Terrace, Ferniegair, Hamilton ML3 7FR

Neil Bielby, 56 Ochiltree, Dunblane FK15 0DF

John Knowler, 3 Balfleurs Street, Milngavie, Glasgow G62 8HW

Craig Macadam, Invertebrate Conservation Trust, Balallan House, 24 Allan Park, Stirling FK8 2QG

John Mitchell, 22 Muirpark Way, Drymen, G63 8HW

Roy Sexton, 22 Alexander Drive, Bridge of Allan, Stirling FK9 4QB

Scott Shanks, Invertebrate Conservation Trust, Balallan House, 24 Allan Park, Stirling FK8 2QG

Heather Young, Butterfly Conservation, Balallan House, 24 Allan Park, Stirling FK8 2QG

DUNBLANE WEATHER REPORT 2013

Neil Bielby

The weather station is my suburban back garden in Ochiltree, Dunblane. This is situated 50 m to the east of the Dunblane Hydro ridge, 100 m a.s.l., in a shallow, sheltered valley. (GR NN 78990143).

I have been recording the weather since 1995 and all averages etc. refer to the last 19 years. (Note: because there is much variation from year to year in Britain in the parameters used to define climate, climatological averages are usually taken over periods of 30 years for temperature and 35 years for rainfall. Therefore, all averages in this report should be viewed with some caution). I am indebted to Dr. John P. Holland for providing automatic Met Office data and additional weather records from Kirkton Farm, Strathfillan (NN 359283; 170 m a.s.l.) and Killin. Weather recording began in 1991 at Kirkton Farm and means etc. for this site date from that year. Killin means date from 2000. The data from Kirkton (this is close to Tyndrum – the latter name being used by the Met Office for online data from this station) allows for some interesting meteorological comparisons between the far north-west and central areas of our region.

Daily rainfall (> 0.2 mm), maximum and minimum temperatures, barometric pressure, cloud cover, wind direction and speed (Beaufort scale) are recorded. All except the maximum daily temperature are recorded at 09.00 hours. A brief description of the day's weather is also noted along with exceptional and unusual weather phenomena across the UK. Unless indicated otherwise, daily (24 hour) rainfall amounts are measured from 09.00 hours on the date mentioned until 09.00 hours the following morning.

2013 was cooler and drier than normal. The mean temperature of 7.99°C (7.88°C Kirkton) was 0.44°C below the average with a high of 29.0°C (9th July) and a low of –8.9°C (12th March). There were 91 air-frosts (average = 72), 3 ground frosts while snow lay on the ground at 09.00 hours on 20 occasions. The 989.0 mm (2,384.0 mm Kirkton) of precipitation was 89 % of the norm with measurable amounts on 196 days (54 %; average = 207; 57 %). Ten months (including the first nine) had precipitation totals lower than their norms while that for December was the highest for that month and the second highest ever. The maximum 24 hour total (09.00-09.00) was 36.4 mm (29th December). The average air pressure was very close to the norm at 1011.8 mb with a high of 1040 mb (25th November) and a record low of 952 mb (27th December).

At Kirkton, the highest temperature recorded was 27.7°C (19th July) with a low of –8.4°C (12th March). Air frosts were recorded on 96 days. Precipitation of 2,384.0 mm was 94 % of the 1991-2010 average with measurable amounts on 275 days (75.5 %).

Lying some 13.5 miles (21.6 km) to the east of Kirkton, Killin (at the head of L. Tay), received 76 % of the formers precipitation in 2013.

Turning to the seasons: Winter (December-February) was warmer and slightly wetter than usual with December 2012 accounting for 58 % of the precipitation whereas February had less than half the norm. Spring (March-May) was cooler and drier than usual with the mean temperature being 1.86°C and precipitation 21 % below their norms respectively. The mean temperature for March was 3.07°C lower than normal. The mean summer temperature (June-August) was above normal but rainfall was only 62 % of the average making this the driest summer since 1996. The mean July temperature was 2.08°C above the norm. Autumn (September- November) was a little cooler and drier than usual with the mean temperature for November being 2.07°C below the norm. (Monthly temperature and precipitation details can be found in Table 1 with a graphic depiction of rainfall amounts in Figure 1).

January was a little milder and drier than usual. The mean temperature of 2.39°C (3.27°C Kirkton) was 0.12°C above the norm. The maximum temperature was 10.0°C, 3rd (10.7°C Kirkton, 8th) while the minimum temperature was –5.3°C (–3.4°C Kirkton, 16th). There were 17 air-frosts and snow lay on the ground on 10 mornings. Precipitation of 98.5 mm (252.0 mm Kirkton) was 83 % of normal with measurable amounts on 21 days. Across Scotland it was marginally warmer and drier than average. It was also a relatively dull month with 74 % of average sunshine.

The year's weather started on a quiet note as a ridge of high pressure developed (1030 mb, 4th). South-westerly winds brought mild air up from the Azores (10.0°C; 13.0°C Aberdeen, 3rd; 14.5°C Colwyn Bay, N. Wales, 2nd) but the weak winter sun only appeared sporadically. The calm, settled weather continued until the 13th with very little sunshine. Maximum daytime temperatures fell from 8.7°C (8th) to 3.3°C (12th). There was a thin covering of wet snow on the morning of the 13th but while England, Wales and Eastern Scotland received varying amounts of snow, some substantial, this station remained dry, calm but cold. Temperatures ranged from –5.3°C to 2.0°C (–13.1°C Braemar, 16th).

Raw easterly winds on the 18th heralded a change with a light dusting of snow in the evening. Snow flurries during the 19th continued during the 20th with an accumulation of 6.0 cm by 09.00 hours on the 21st when it continued to snow all day. England bore the brunt of the wintery weather with the A68 and A66 trunk roads closed and c.5,000 schools also closed (only 30 were in Scotland). Several airports across England were severely affected by lying snow with Heathrow faring worst as hundreds of flights were cancelled. While there was a slow thaw here on the 22nd/23rd the easterly winds meant it was the turn of the Eastern Borders and Aberdeenshire to receive the bulk of the snow with an accumulation of 40.0 cm at Balmoral and c.150 schools being closed throughout both areas. Temperatures dropped to –13.6°C in Hertfordshire (22nd).

An Atlantic front reached the UK early on the 25th and rain on western coasts quickly turned to snow as it moved inland. There was light to medium snowfall in Dunblane throughout the day but it was heavier on higher ground – Eskdalemuir recording a depth of 30 cm. Aberdeen airport was closed for several hours and in the evening, heavy snowfall in NE England brought the M6 near Manchester to a standstill. The morning of the 26th saw some rare sunshine but thickening cloud during the afternoon heralded the arrival of another Atlantic weather system. This deep low (975 mb) brought much milder air and steady rain which produced a rapid thaw of lying snow during the night of the 26th/27th.

Yet another Atlantic weather system on the 29th/30th brought storm force winds to the north and west of Scotland with gusts of up to 86 mph recorded in the Outer Hebrides, Orkneys and Shetland. The causeways in the Uists and on Orkney were closed to traffic while a wind speed of 135 mph was recorded on Cairngorm summit. It was also wet from the 26th to the month end and while this station received only 33.1 mm during this period Kirkton totalled 163.4 mm.

February was colder and drier than usual with the mean temperature of 1.74°C (2.36°C Kirkton) being 1.29°C below the average. Total precipitation of 43.6 mm (106.2 mm Kirkton) was only 46 % of the norm with measurable amounts on 10 days. There were 18 frosts (average 13) while snow lay on the ground at 09.00 hours on three occasions. Pressure ranged from 896 mb to 1039 mb. Across Scotland the mean temperature was 0.5°C below the 1981-2010 average with 61 % of the long-term average precipitation. It was the 4th sunniest February in a series dating back to 1929.

A brief ridge of high pressure on the 2nd (1016 mb) gave a rare sunny day. A very deep low off Greenland (4th) produced 70 mph plus winds in the Western and Northern Isles with waves of up to 20 metres; the latter destroying a wall at the lighthouse on Fair Isle which had stood for 122 years. Here, sleet showers during the day turned to snow which gave a 1.0 cm covering at 09.00 hours (5th). It continued snowing that morning but cleared to a sunny afternoon with temperatures rising to 5.0°C which caused a rapid melt.

The 6th was a very clear, sunny day with a bitingly cold northerly airflow. The next 3 days were calm and damp with light rain during the night. In the early hours of the 13th, rain on an Atlantic front turned to snow as it moved inland. By noon that day 8.0 cm of wet snow had accumulated (22.0 cm at Whitehillocks, Angus). In the afternoon the snow turned to sleet, then rain and with temperatures rising during the night, the lying snow had virtually disappeared by 09.00 hours on the 14th. The weather remained on the mild side (8.6°C, 15th) with several sunny, spring-like days until the 19th (13.9°C Kinlochewe, 17th). High pressure (1039 mb, 26th) persisted until the month end with regular night frosts (–6.6°C, 19th; –10.0°C Aviemore, 22nd) and often sunny but cool days. It remained mostly calm with occasional, light E or SE breezes during the day. There was no precipitation during the last 14 days of the month. Fog in the Carse of Stirling on the 27th and 28th was slow to clear.

March was notably colder and drier than usual. The mean temperature of 1.73°C (1.52°C Kirkton) was 3.12°C below the average making this the coldest March at this station (after 2.57°C, March 1995). There were 20 air-frosts while snow lay on the ground at 09.00 hours on six occasions. Total precipitation of 40.9 mm (52.2 mm Kirkton) was 60 % of the norm with recordable amounts on 14 days. At Kirkton it was the coldest month of the year and the coldest March in a series dating from 1991. Precipitation at Kirkton was only 22 % of the March norm.

The first two days of the month were sunny but as the high pressure system decayed it became permanently overcast with light rain/drizzle on raw easterly breezes. 0.5 mm of rain on the 6th brought to an end 20 days without precipitation. A north-easterly airstream on the 10th delivered regular snow showers with a covering of one cm of fine snow at 09.00 hours on the 11th. Clear skies during the night of the 11th/12th saw the thermometer plummet to –8.9°C (–8.4°C Kirkton), the lowest temperature of the winter. A combination of a south-westerly airstream and falling barometric pressure brought dull and damp conditions on the 14th and 15th but the reinstatement of north-easterlies on the 16th produced snow (not settling) until mid-aft when it turned to rain. The easterly airstream persisted until the end of the month producing snow flurries most days on bitterly cold winds.

More persistent snow during the night of the 18th/19th had produced 6.5 mm of lying snow by 09.00 on the 19th. As would be expected, the east coast bore the brunt of both the wind and snow but, during the early hours of the 22nd, snow on south-easterly gales produced blizzard conditions in SW Scotland with several main roads becoming impassable and c.10,000 homes in the region losing power including the whole of the island of Arran where power was not restored to all until the 26th. Towards the end of the month the winds moderated and with clearer skies temperatures dropped to –7.2°C (30th; –12.0°C Braemar, 31st).

April was colder than normal with the mean temperature of 5.9°C (4.96°C Kirkton) being 1.92°C below the average. The lowest temperature was –4.2°C (6th) with a high of 14.2°C (18th). There were 11 air frosts (average = 5). Precipitation of 61.2 mm (247.8 mm Kirkton, 66 % above the norm) was just below the average with measurable amounts on 18 days. The highest daily rainfall amount was 16.8 mm (17th). Scotland wide the mean temperature was 1.3°C below the 1981-2010 average with 133 % of average rainfall with the north and west being particularly wet. All areas (apart from the Borders) had above average amounts of sunshine with Northern Scotland enjoying its sunniest April since 1974. Across the UK the average temperature was similar to April 2012 and the coldest since 1989. The highest temperature recorded was in Faversham (Kent) with 23.1°C (25th) whilst the coldest was –11.2°C at

Braemar (2nd). In the 24 hours ending at 09.00 on the 17th, 63.6 mm of rain fell at Lusa, Skye.

High pressure and the easterly airstream continued until the 11th. It was mostly sunny but the cool easterly breezes and nightly frosts (–4.2°C; –6.1°C Kirkton, 6th) kept temperatures down as the daily maximum temperature slowly increased from 6.4° (1st) to 9.8°C (6th). There was no measurable precipitation during the first 9 days. A south-westerly airstream predominated for the rest of the month providing classic April weather of sunshine and showers. There were strong south-westerly winds on the 16th (72 mph at Inverbervie, Angus) followed the next day by heavy rain (16.8 mm; 46.6 mm Kirkton). There were two heavy hail showers on the 26th.

May was a little cooler and drier than normal. The mean temperature of 10.2°C (9.42°C Kirkton) was 0.72°C below the mean with a high of 22.6°C (20th) and a low of –0.7°C (15th). There was one air and one ground frost. Rainfall of 59.3 mm (170.6 mm Kirkton) was 86 % of the norm with measurable amounts on 16 days. In Scotland, the mean temperature was 0.4°C below the 1981-2010 average while across the UK it was 0.8°C cooler at 9.5°C, making it the coldest May since 1996. A maximum temperature of 23.8°C was recorded at Drumburgh, Cumbria (7th) and a low of –5.5°C at Alston, Cumbria (2nd).

The weather continued in an unsettled mode with a band of heavy rain between 12.00-20.00 on the 3rd depositing 14.5 mm (28.8 mm Kirkton). An Atlantic airstream ensured that the weather continued unsettled until the 18th with regular fronts passing through Scotland producing spells of rain, these being heaviest in the west. The 7th was a rare warm, dry day with the promise of summer as the temperature climbed to 21.0° C (21.4°C Kinlochewe). After heavy rain during the afternoon, evening and night of the 18th (17.0 mm) the weather slowly improved as the barometric pressure built. The 20th was a humid day (22.6°C) while strong, cold northerly winds on the 23rd produced a wintery feel with a maximum temperature of only 10.9°C. The 25th was a rare cloudless day. A slow-moving front produced some rain on the 27th when a maximum temperature of only 10.5°C was recorded. Building high pressure then ensued with no measurable rain falling during the final 4 days of the month and temperatures reaching 22.4°C (30th).

June was warmer and much drier than usual with the mean temperature of 14.08°C (12.43°C Kirkton) being 0.16°C above the norm. Rainfall of 27.5 mm (51.4 mm Kirkton) was only 37 % of the average with measurable amounts on only 10 days. Barometric pressure ranged from 995 mb to 1033 mb.

High pressure remained over the country for the first 8 days of the month giving dry and warm weather with several sunny 'summer' days. Temperatures peaked at 25.1°C, 8th (22.4°C Kirkton), the warmest day of the year to date. The mornings were mostly calm with north-easterly breezes picking up during the day. It then became more unsettled as pressure fell culminating in heavy rain during the night of the 14th/15th. Maximum daytime temperatures ranged from 18.1°C to 19.8°C between the 9th and 14th but the 15th was a cold, grey day when temperatures only reached 10.3°C. From the 16th to the 21st the weather was mostly sunny and warm (23.5°C, 17th) but rain during the night of the 21st/22nd heralded a change to more unsettled, cooler conditions which persisted until the month end.

July was warmer and a little drier than normal with the mean temperature of 17.97°C (16.12°C Kirkton) being 2.08°C above the average making this the warmest July since 2006. Precipitation of 77.5 mm (94.6 mm Kirkton) was 91 % of the norm (84 % for Scotland overall) and fell at the start and end of the month. Across Scotland it was the warmest July since 2006 and the 2nd warmest on record in a sequence dating back to 1910. It was also the 3rd sunniest July in Scotland on record. UK wide it was the 3rd warmest July (after 1983 and 2006) with a mean temperature of 17.0°C in a series also dating back to 1910.

The unsettled weather continued until the 5th when high pressure started to build over the UK. Daytime temperatures also climbed with year high's continually being set: 27.6°C (8th); 29.0°C (9th; 29.3°C Grangemouth – the hottest place in the UK that day). Year UK highs were also breached with 29.7°C at Bournemouth (7th); 31.4°C Heathrow (13th); 32.2°C London (17th). These often hot, mostly sunny conditions, lasted until the 23rd with 18 consecutive days without rain. This was the hottest spell of weather in the UK since 2006 with the temperature reaching at least 28°C somewhere in the UK on 19 consecutive days. The highest temperature recorded in Scotland was 30.5°C in Kirkcudbrightshire (19th) while in the UK it was 33.5°C at Heathrow (22nd).

The hot, dry spell finally ended on the 23rd with a downpour at noon (60.4 mm Livingston Mill, West Lothian). An unsettled spell then ensued as an Atlantic low replaced the high pressure system. With temperatures remaining above the norm for the time of year it became humid which triggered thunderstorms across Scotland. Some of these were violent causing localized flooding. At this station, one such deposited 10.0 mm of rain and hail in 20 minutes at 13.30 on the 26th. A more generalized band of rain moving up from England produced 13.4 mm between 21.30 on the 27th to noon the following day. With a low pressure system remaining just to the west of the UK, the weather continued unsettled until the month end although it remained fairly warm, especially when the sun did break through.

August was a little warmer but much drier than the norm. The mean temperature of 15.6°C (13.97°C Kirkton) was 0.34°C above average while rainfall of 48.4 mm (133.4 mm Kirkton) was only 54 % of the average making this the driest August since 2003 (24.3 mm). The mean pressure of 1013 mb was equal to the overall mean.

Rain, heavy at times, starting at 19.00 hours on the 31st July continued until 14.30 hours the following day depositing 27.0 mm. Thereafter, with the jetstream over the UK, the weather remained a little unsettled, although the Stirling area avoided much of the wetter weather to the north and west, receiving only the occasional shower or short spell of rain until the 25th when a ridge of high pressure introduced a more settled spell for 3 days. Temperatures were a little cooler ranging from 18.0°C to 22.8°C but feeling warm in the sun on calm days. A south-westerly airstream predominated throughout this period.

From the 28th to the month end, frontal systems crossing the north-west of Scotland brought cooler, cloudier conditions to the Stirling area although rainfall was infrequent with only small amounts. The 31st was noticeably cooler with a maximum temperature of only 15.5°C.

September was slightly cooler and noticeably drier than average. The mean temperature of 11.91°C (11.49°C Kirkton) was 0.24°C below the mean with a daytime high of 20.7°C (22nd) and a night low of 2.6°C (14th). Rainfall of 62.9 mm (140.2 mm Kirkton) was 72 % of the mean with measurable amounts falling on 14 days (mean = 16). Atmospheric pressure ranged from 990 mb to 1025 mb with a mean of 1013 mb. Across Scotland it was the driest September since 2003 with 70 % of the average rainfall.

The 1st was appropriately cool and autumnal with a maximum temperature of 14.7°C. The next 3 days were warmer (21.0°C; 24.7°C Fyvie Castle, Aberdeenshire 3rd) and mostly sunny if breezy before cooler conditions returned. Heavy rain from 19.00 on the 6th produced 16.0 mm in 14 hours (71.0 mm Nunraw Abbey, East Lothian). Thereafter the weather remained relatively 'quiet' with rain most days but amounts were normally small – the highest being 11.0 mm on the 14th. Winds were mostly light and from a south-westerly direction until the 24th after which an easterly airflow between an anticyclone over Scandinavia and low pressure systems in the Atlantic pertained until the month end.

October was milder and wetter than average. The mean temperature of 9.63°C (9.69°C Kirkton) was 1.13°C above the norm with the mean daily low of 6.9°C being 1.62°C above average and the mean daily high of 12.35°C being 0.63°C above average. A high temperature of 17.6°C (4th) and a low of –2.2°C were recorded, this latter being the only air-frost. Rainfall of 181.1 mm (281.6 mm Kirkton) was 33 % above the mean with measurable amounts on 23 days making this the wettest month since December 2012. Mean pressure was 1003.0 mb with a high of 1033 mb and a low of 978 mb. Across Scotland the mean temperature was 1.4°C above the 1981-2010 average but rainfall was just 3 % above the norm compared to plus 27 % for the UK as a whole.

Heavy pulses of rain during the evening/nights of the 2nd/3rd and 3rd/4th deposited 34.9 mm (53.6 mm Kirkton), the first substantial amount since the beginning of August (66.4 mm at Benmore, Argyll where the A83 was yet again closed by a landslip at the Rest and be Thankful). The weather continued a little unsettled until the 8th when high pressure built over the North Atlantic and a low developed over Norway. This drew down cold northerly winds on the 9th and 10th. From the 9th to the 13th the days were mostly unbroken sunshine and the clear skies produced the first frost of the autumn on the morning of the 11th (–2.2°C). Easterly winds pertained from the 11th-13th bringing a blanket of cloud from the SE during the afternoon of the 13th. A largely stationary low pressure system then established itself to the west of the British Isles and slow moving fronts associated with it and further Atlantic lows deposited various amounts of rain daily until the 29th. The 19th was a particularly wet day with 23.0 mm deposited during the 24 hours from 09.00. A south-westerly airstream dominated during this period which kept temperatures above the seasonal norm with a high of 14.8°C (20th). Another moisture laden front produced 33.7 mm of rain during the 16 hours from 16.00 hours on the 21st (37.0 mm Eskdalemuir). Pressure at 09.00 on the 23rd fell to 981 mb; its lowest level since the 27th of January. Another deep low on the 28th (978.0 mb) led to storm force winds across the south of England (80 mph) that day with a gust of 99 mph recorded at the Needles (Isle of Wight). At one point c.600,000 homes were without power. Four people were killed by falling trees and there was widespread structural damage. Scotland escaped this storm but the unsettled weather continued with the 29th being a rare dry day.

November was colder and drier than normal. The mean temperature of 2.5°C (3.41°C Kirkton) was 2.07°C below the norm with a mean low of –0.74°C and a mean high of 5.73°C. The lowest temperature was –7.4°C (22nd) and the highest 11.1°C (27th). There were 19 air-frosts (average 9). Total rainfall of 62.6 mm (202.8 mm Kirkton) was only 55 % of the average with measurable amounts on 15 days.

Regular Atlantic depressions kept the weather largely unsettled although this area escaped the much wetter conditions affecting the north-west of Scotland and southern England. The 3rd and the 4th were scarce dry days with unbroken sunshine and temperatures were notably lower with several frosts (–5.7°C, 5th). The weather then became relatively quiet for November with occasional night frosts and the odd mild day (10.7°C, 11th.)

A vigorous front crossed south across Scotland during the night of the 19th/20th depositing 11.0 mm of rain. An unstable polar airstream followed in its wake with biting northerly winds producing gusts which were violent enough to bring down branches and the odd tree during the night of the 20th/21st. Subsequently, high pressure built from the west accompanied by night frosts (–7.4°C, 22nd; –7.7°C Kirkton) and a continuation of the sunny, calm days which had largely been the norm since the 17th. This settled spell lasted until the month end with only two weak fronts bringing a little rain and overcast conditions. There was dense fog in the Carse of Stirling during the morning of the 25th.

December was milder and much wetter than usual. The mean temperature of 4.52°C (5.47°C Kirkton) was 2.66°C above the average making this the warmest December at this station. The minimum temperature of 10.3°C (recorded between 09.00 hours on the 12th to 09.00 hours on the 13th) was the highest ever in a 24 hour period for this month. There were only 4 air-frosts (average 15) and only one occasion when snow lay on the ground at 09.00 hours. Rainfall of 225.5 mm (651.2 mm Kirkton) was 103 % more than the norm making this the wettest ever December with measurable amounts on 28 days. Barometric pressure of 952 mb at 09.00 hours on the 27th was the lowest ever recorded here. Across Scotland the mean temperature was 2.3°C above the 1981-2010 average making it the 5th mildest December since 1910. At Kirkton, precipitation was more than double the 20 year average while, for Scotland, it was 81 % above the norm making it the wettest December in a series also dating from 1910.

A high pressure system over the UK (1031 mb, 2nd) meant settled weather for the first 4 days of the month, two of which were largely sunny.

Storm force winds associated with a vigorous Atlantic low pressure system crossed Scotland from north to south during the early morning of the 5th. Gusts of 116 mph and 106 mph were reported from Stornaway and Glen Ogle respectively. The height of the storm coincided with the morning rush hour in the Central Belt of Scotland causing much travel chaos. All train services were suspended until mid-afternoon; the Skye, Dornoch, Kessock, Tay, Friarton and Erskine bridges were closed to all traffic (an articulated lorry was blown over on the Friarton Bridge at Perth with several other lorries being blown over across Scotland); 130,000 homes were without power including some in Dunblane and 195 schools were closed.

Winds of over 80 mph were recorded throughout the Central Belt with a gust of 91 mph on the Forth Road Bridge. These winds brought down many trees which blocked roads and railway lines – there were reports of garden trampolines careering across the countryside. Heavy rain (19.0 mm; 57.4 mm Kirkton) accompanied this depression with flooding in some places. Gusts of over 140 mph were recorded on Aonach Mór near Fort William. A storm surge affected North Sea coasts with thousands of homes evacuated and several houses collapsing into the sea due to erosion.

A cold north-westerly airstream followed in the wake of the storm dragging down Arctic air and with it sporadic short, light snow showers which produced a thin covering – the first of the winter.

From the 8th until the month end a continuous conveyor belt of Atlantic depressions and associated fronts swept across Scotland bringing south-westerly winds, rain and above average temperatures – a high of 16.6°C was recorded in Sutherland (9th). The 14th was a particularly wild day of driving rain (19.0 mm; 38.2 mm Kirkton). The night of the 18th/19th was also particularly windy with gusts of up to 90 mph recorded in South Uist and

60 mph in Glasgow. Further heavy rain (11.0 mm Dunblane; 44.2 mm Kirkton) on the 20th left the ground saturated with standing water widespread.

Heavy rain and gale force winds which swept across the south of England during the 23rd continued through the night resulting in widespread travel chaos south of the M4 corridor the following morning. Train services were suspended to enable lines to be cleared of fallen trees and many roads were impassable due to flooding – especially in Dorset. Over 1,000 homes were inundated with flood water with c.100,000 without electricity while a cross-channel ferry had to ride out the storm outside Dover through the night.

A particularly deep low on the 24th produced the lowest ever recorded barometric pressure here at 957 mb (936 mb Stornaway – the lowest at a UK land station for 'many years'). The accompanying strong winds gusted to 82 mph in Peterhead. While rainfall amounts in Dunblane were moderate (4.5 mm) Kirkton received 50.0 mm. Christmas Day was relatively calm with some weak winter sunshine and the occasional light shower. Yet another intense low pressure system on the 27th saw the barometer record another new low at 952 mb with accompanying gales (81 mph Inverbervie, Angus). 77.0 mm of rain fell at Kirkton in the 36 hour period from 21.00 on the 26th while heavy and persistent rain during the evening/night of the 29th/30th produced 36.4 mm in Dunblane and severe flooding in parts of SW Scotland and the Glasgow area.

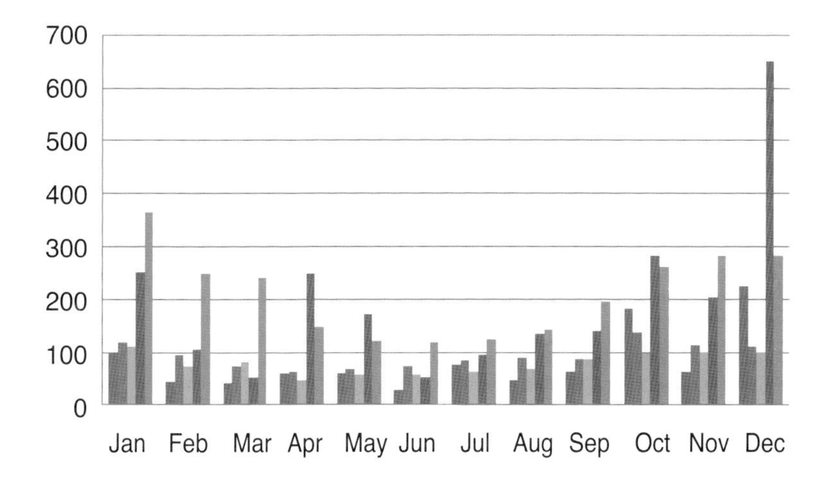

Dunblane 2013

Dunblane mean (1995-2013)

Parkhead mean (1971-2000)

Kirkton 2013

Kirkton mean (1991-2010)

Figure 1. Rainfall 2013

Table 1. Temperature and precipitation 2013. Climatological Station Dunblane.

	Temp Mean minima	Temp Mean maxima	Number of air frosts	Total precipitation (mm)		Greatest 24 hour total (mm)	Number of days of measurable precipitation
January	0.86 (0.07)	3.92 (4.47)	17/14 (15)	98.5/252.0	(118.7/364.2)	16.1 (35.0)	21/25 (20)
February	-1.46 (0.17)	4.93 (3.03)	18/19 (13)	43.6/106.2	(94.2/247.9)	18.8 (38.0)	10/18 (17)
March	-1.35 (1.21)	4.8 (8.5)	20/22 (11)	40.9/52.2	(73.8/239.6)	9.3 (30.5)	14/20 (16)
April	1.39 (3.35)	10.41 (12.3)	11/11 (5)	61.2/247.8	(63.0/148.9)	16.8 (27.8)	18/22 (15)
May	5.27 (5.76)	15.13 (16.08)	1/2 (2)	59.3/170.6	(69.0/120.3)	17.0 (27.1)	16/25 (17)
June	8.62 (8.83)	19.53 (19.01)	0/0 (0)	27.5/51.4	(74.3/118.1)	7.0 (39.8)	10/13 (15)
July	12.59 (10.79)	23.34 (20.98)	0/0 (0)	77.5/94.6	(85.4/124.1)	13.5 (33.5)	13/17 (16)
August	11.03 (10.53)	20.17 (19.98)	0/0 (0)	48.4/133.4	(88.9/143.1)	13.7 (40.0)	14/29 (16)
September	7.97 (8.35)	15.84 (15.94)	0/1 (<1)	62.9/140.2	(88.1/196.3)	16.0 (36.5)	14/22 (16)
October	6.9 (5.28)	12.35 (11.72)	1/3 (4)	181.7/281.6	(136.5/261.8)	33.7 (41.9)	23/28 (22)
November	-0.74 (1.88)	5.73 (7.25)	19/19 (7)	62.6/202.8	(113.6/282.0)	12.0 (39)	15/26 (20)
December	2.54 (-0.27)	6.49 (4.0)	4/5 (15)	225.5/651.2	(111.2/281.9)	36.4 (36.4)	28/30 (19)
Year	4.4 (4.73)	11.59 (12.13)	91/96 (72)	989.0/2384.0	(1117.4/2528.2)	36.4 (41.9)	196/275 (207)

The climatological means for Dunblane are shown in ( ). Where either two 2013 values or climatological means are given, the first relates to Dunblane and the second to Kirkton. Figure in parenthesis in the 'Greatest 24 hour total (mm)' table refer to the highest ever 24 hour value for that month at Dunblane (09.00 hours to 09.00 hours). Figure in parenthesis in the 'Number of days of measurable precipitation' refer to Dunblane. Temperatures are given in degrees Celsius.

Plant Report 2014

CHANGES IN THE KING'S PARK FLORA DURING THE LAST HUNDRED YEARS

Roy Sexton
Stirling Members Centre, Scottish Wildlife Trust

In 1908 Alexander Moyes read a paper entitled the *Wild flowers of King's Park* to the March meeting of Stirling Natural History and Archaeological Society (Moyes, 1908). Moyes who served for 40 years as headmaster of the primary section of the High School had been a founding member of the Society in 1877-8 and became its vice president in 1905. He lived conveniently close to the Park at 22 Douglas Terrace which bears a plaque to commemorate the loss of his son William a senior engineer aboard the Titanic.

Accompanying Moyes description was a list of 228 species of flowering plants which he had noted in King's Park over many previous years. As an extension of a wildlife recording day arranged by Stirling Ranger Service and Friends of King's Park (FKP), the local group of the Scottish Wildlife Trust (SWT) undertook to resurvey the Park's flora and compare the results with Moyes 1908 account. Twenty outings were organized involving 17 recorders. Among these were Liz Lavery of the Botanical Society of Britain and Ireland (BSBI), Sue Sexton, Janet Harbidge, Roy Anderson and Tony Rogers of the SWT and the local Biodiversity Officer Guy Harewood and his team.

King's Park is Scotland's most ancient Royal Park having been enclosed as royal hunting grounds between 1165 and 1174. Because the boundaries have changed over the years the area referred to as King's Park is variable. This survey included the land currently occupied by the Stirling Golf Club course and the associated Council recreation areas together with the surrounding wooded cliffs and a narrow peripheral strip of fields. It is bounded by the A811 Dumbarton Road to the north, Victoria Place to the east, King's Park Road to the south east and the 17thC Royal Park boundary wall behind Douglas Terrace to the southwest (Figure 1). Ornamental gardens were not included.

King's Park together with Abbey Craig and Stirling Castle Rock are outcroppings of an intrusive slab of quartz dolerite known as the 'Stirling Sill'. The sill was formed from molten rock which rose through the bedding planes in the base of the Carboniferous sequence during the late Carboniferous – early Permian period. Most of the overlying softer sedimentary rocks were swept away during the glaciations leaving a hard sloping surface dipping from 70 m in the SW to 30 m in the NE. Around the edge of the sill a horseshoe shaped rim of cliffs runs from King's Park Farm to Douglas Terrace. Dolerite weathers badly and this has caused large boulders to detach and accumulate around the

Figure 1. Ordnance Survey map of King's Park of 1896. Note that the 9 hole golf course is restricted to the southern edge of the site the main area being occupied by the old horse racing course. The whole of this central area was grazed. The curling ponds, rifle range and flagstaff and sand quarry referred to in the account are also shown. Reproduced by permission of the National Library of Scotland.

base of the cliffs. Originally areas of the cliff on the north side were quarried, a process which ceased as a result of public protest in about 1894. In 1908 they also served as a backstop for the rifle range which was located near the Homesteads greenhouses.

As Moyes (1908) pointed out soil characteristics are important in determining the plant species that are able to grow on them and he went on to describe what was known of their origins. Over the intervening century our understanding has improved and environmental scientist Dr Richard Tipping provided the following brief update: *After the last glaciation 6,500 years ago the sea level was initially up to 12 m higher than today and the elevated area of King's Park formed the southern and eastern shore of a marine embayment that stretched to Arnprior far to the west. The rock outcrops west of Kings Park Farm formed the sea-cliffs. The old town of Stirling, on the hill, was a peninsula jutting into the sea. Its eastern side fell to the sea at Braehead. The clays and silts in the fields round the base of the cliffs beside the A811 Dumbarton Road were formed in this shallow sea. The valley between the golf course and Castle Rock is filled with sands and gravels issuing from meltwater streams as the ice retreated westward. The quarry behind Douglas Terrace (in use in 1896) exploited sand deposited in the same way.* More detail can be found in SNH's booklet *Loch Lomond to Stirling: A Landscape Fashioned by Geology* which is available on line.

Local soil scientist Andrew Hipkin provided the following account of the golf course plateau soils which developed on the hard dolerite rocks exposed after the glaciation: *Dolerite contains plagioclase felspar and augite (pyroxene) with other associated minerals. These weather to give varying amounts of calcium, magnesium, sodium, iron and potassium which are important in plant nutrition. The relatively high calcium and magnesium gives rise to a pH in the range 6 to 7, which increases with depth. These friable soils are often shallow over rock, but are relatively nutrient-rich, especially when compared to those developed on local weathered sandstone. The iron content in the dolerite is responsible for the soil's attractive brown colour.*

An understanding of the changes in the flora of the Park requires a knowledge of its use over the intervening century. The leaflet produced by the Friends of King's Park provided a rich source of information (Wilson and Becci, 2010). In addition local historian John Harrison joined us prior to the first surveying day and discussed what the Park would have been like in 1908 as well as the main changes that have taken place since. Dorothy Wilson who has been actively researching the area has also provided answers to many important questions. The following is a brief summary of the relevant information gathered from these sources:

Rig and furrow marking indicate that extensive areas of the current golf course/recreational areas were originally cultivated. By the 1850s most of the park was let out as pasture but Moyes pointed out that some weeds in his list like restharrow were relics of this previous use for arable crops. The cattle were probably originally controlled by a herdsman who lived in the 'Herds Hoose' – beautifully painted by Leonard Baker in the mid 1860s (Plate 4). This had been demolished well before 1908 and fencing introduced to restrain the cattle. In the face of local opposition some 12.5 hectares in the eastern part of the park were ploughed up during the 1914-18 war. The exercise was not repeated in the 1939-45 war because it produced *lamentable returns* and would have resulted in a reduction in the dairy herd .

The main expanse of the park inside the cliffs was almost treeless in 1908 and the two ancient hawthorns shown in the Baker's picture were mentioned as conspicuous landmarks by Moyes. As can be seen from the 1896 OS map (Figure 1) a horse racing circuit ran through the current golf course area. This had been improved in 1800 when the loch in the NE corner of the Park was drained and an embankment constructed through it to level the track. These races were very popular and crowds of 30,000 were recorded. The last was held in 1854 and the grandstand burned down in 1872. Moyes records that near the grandstand there had been a colony of sweet violets (*Viola odorata*) which had recently disappeared.

Although golf had been played on the park since at least the early 17C the first formal 7 hole course was established in 1869 in the SW corner (Figure 1). This was extended first to a 9 hole course in 1877 and then doubled in size to an 18 hole course in 1912 i.e. after Moyes' account. This new course occupied the same area as that existing today though in 1960 the layout was extensively redesigned. Originally the course was grazed by cattle, the greens being protected by wire fencing. A young 1950s golfer related that he was scared of being caught in the daily stampede that occurred when the herd of Ayrshire dairy cattle was called into King's Park Farm. Although the grazing rights were bought out by the golf club, stray cattle and sheep were still common until the 1970s.

An account of the maintenance of Scottish golf courses by Bowie (2014) describes how originally the natural vegetation of golf courses was kept short by cattle, rabbits and scythes and would have been rich in short wild flowers. The early heavy lawn mowers developed in the 1830s were initially considered inferior to a good green keeper with a scythe, however more efficient machines slowly took over from the 1880s and these were being powered by petrol engines after the first world war (Arthur, 2014). By the 1950s the fairways were cut with towed gang mowers.

The conversion of flower rich meadow grassland into grass rich golf course sward was initially facilitated by the use of sand dressings. This encouraged finer deep rooting colonial bent (*Agrostis spp*) and fescue grasses (*Festuca spp*) discouraging rye grass (*Lolium spp*) and annual meadow grass (*Poa annua*). During the early 1920s dressings first contained phosphate, then nitrogen and potash fertilisers. The greens would have been initially hand weeded to remove chickweed and daisies and close scything got rid of white clover. The extremely effective selective herbicides like 2,4 D which are used to kill off non-grass species became available after the second world war. The construction of the modern golf course has also involved smoothing out the natural rock outcrops and drainage of lower ground. The development of power trenching machines to lay tile drains in the 1900s and aeration machines in the 1930s were important in this respect. All this has resulted in massive changes to the flora of the greens and fairways which lost most of their broad-leaved flowering plants and became predominately grass. Of 600 random survey points on the fairways none included anything but grass though there were rare islands where some broad-leaved species still persist. Another major change in the golf and recreation area was the planting of trees. An aerial photograph taken in 1947 shows only one tree. Presumably when grazing was still practised any tree seedling that appeared was quickly consumed. Today there are well over 500 mostly native trees largely introduced in plantings since 1980 though a few have naturally regenerated from wind and bird dispersed seed.

Moyes (1908) listed 228 species of wild flowering plants in King's Park however taxonomists have reclassified some of them so the modern day equivalent would include 225 species (see appendix). Our 2014 list includes 247 species, so superficially it appears that the floral biodiversity has shown a welcome increase. Unfortunately only 144 plants from the original 1908 list remain (see appendix) and all but one of the 81 that have been lost are native species. Of the 103 new species found in 2014 half are non-native or foreign plants that have largely been planted or have spread from neighbouring gardens (see appendix).

Moyes only identified three non-native garden plants which had spread into the Park. He thought cotoneaster seeds had been brought by birds from a Coney Park Nursery situated just over the Park's southwest wall. At this time cotoneaster was only recorded at one other wild site in North Wales. Today *Cotoneaster simonsii* and *C. horizontalis* have become invasive pests, both of which have been recorded in a quarter of all BSBI's British 10 km survey squares.

Of the fifty modern non-native introductions many are garden ornamentals such as snowdrops, daffodils, tulips, buddleja, leopardsbane, snowberry, lilac, periwinkle, etc. Not all of these should be dismissed as detrimental to our native wildlife. For example flowering currant, cotoneaster and mahonia are favoured nectaring plants for bees as is buddleja for butterflies. Alien species can also make very attractive additions to our native flora and in spring curtains of colourful climbing plants such as aubretia, yellow corydalis, ivy-leaved toadflax, fairy foxglove and northern rock-cress hang from the lime rich mortar in the old Park wall. Amongst the non-native trees planted on the golf course/recreational area are: horse chestnut, whitebeam, hybrid lime, larch, Leyland cypress, ornamental cherry and apple. In addition the clumps of evergreen Norwegian and Sitka spruce look particularly inappropriate.

One newcomer which illustrates the speed at which foreign species can spread is pineappleweed a plant of bare ground whose tiny flowers smell of pineapple when crushed. It only escaped from Kew Gardens in 1871 but is now present in 93 % of the 10 km recording squares in the entire British Isles. The explanation for this success was provided by a study in 1964 which showed it was the most common seed carried round the countryside in the tread of wet car tyres (Mabey, 1996). Of the many non-native plants that have been introduced into Scotland a few are considered highly invasive and will overwhelm native plant communities. Several of these are new to the King's Park area and efforts are being made to deal with them before they get out of control. They include giant hogweed, Himalayan balsam, *Rhododrendron ponticum*, pirri-pirri-burr and pick-a-back plant. Japanese knotweed is not present at the moment but there is a big clump in the Haining just across the A811.

Half of the new finds in the 2014 survey are native species some of which are now present in such numbers that it is hard to believe they were not in the Park in 1908. Moyes purposely looked for birch but could not find it, probably because the cattle grazed it off and stopped it becoming established. It is now abundant in the woods, the golf course rough and on the abandoned quarry walls. Another example is rosebay willowherb whose drifts of purple flowers are not only found in the Park but over hectares of waste ground all over the Central Belt of Scotland. In the late 1800s this was a scarce attractive woodland plant which was being cultivated in gardens. At about the time of the first World War it started spreading to recently harvested woodlands and during the second world war it was quick to colonise bomb sites and the railway system. Today clouds of its wind blown seed can be seen drifting over Stirling and these have led to the establishment of colonies on any available waste land including some in the King's Park. The sudden change in this plant's colonial behaviour has puzzled botanists. One hypothesis was that a new more aggressive race was brought in on timber from Canada where it is known as 'fireweed'; however no DNA evidence has been found to support the theory (Mabey, 1996). This explanation does account for the spread of the yellow Welsh poppy which is not only found in King's Park but has become a ubiquitous local garden weed. As its name implies it used to be restricted to a few sites in Wales but like rose bay willowherb it was also grown as an attractive garden ornamental. In this case the DNA analysis has shown that the spreading and garden populations are different to the native Welsh stock but similar to populations found in the Pyrenees, from where it was probably imported by the horticultural trade (Preston et al., 2012).

The modern fashion for planting native species has resulted in the introduction of many native trees on the golf course area. These include Scots pine, ash, oak, beech, mountain ash, birch, elm, sycamore, etc. Two small plots have been seeded with wild flower mixes by FKP to provide nectaring sources for insects. These have reintroduced some local plants like kidney vetch, viper's bugloss, cowslip, and oxeye daisy.

Moyes splits his account of the flora of King's Park into four habitat groupings: wet marshy ground and ponds; wooded slopes; bare and rocky places; grassy slopes and pasture land.

As a result of extensive drainage operations it is the plants of wet places that have suffered the biggest loss of species. The wet hollows in which they once grew on the golf course are a thing of the past. The fields between the A811 and the cliffs to the west of King's Park Farm although partially drained have remained very wet particularly along the base of the cliffs. As a consequence they retained some plants of wet ground like water blinks, marsh-marigold, cuckooflower and meadowsweet. During the last two years these fields have been sprayed with selective herbicides and are currently having more field drains installed. This will probably restrict wetland species to the cliff bases. The infilling of the old curling and farm ponds also eliminated a number of plants which grew there including water plantains, floating sweet grass and duckweed. The situation would have been worse had not a number of species survived in the wet area next to Homesteads including marsh cinquefoil, water cress and yellow iris.

It may come as a relief to find that the wooded slopes between King's Park Farm and Douglas Terrace are still just as Moyes described them. There are probably oaks, sycamores, ash and hazels that have survived the century between the surveys. Elm is not a dominant species so the effects of Dutch elm disease in the 1980s was not as devastating as in other woods in the district. However we must await the impact of the ash dieback disease (*Chalara fraxinea*) which has been reported in Balquhidderock wood. There are over two hundred hazels in King's Park woodland and unless they were deliberately planted it is hard to explain why there are none in the corresponding woodlands round the Castle Rock only a few hundred yards away. Holly and birch are now both quite common but were not present in 1908 and it is hard to offer an explanation of why not. The bushes which form the periphery of the woodland are quite as spectacular as they were in Moyes' time. He describes *the dazzling white blossoms of blackthorn or sloe which herald the start of spring* and later in the season in April and early May how *the woods are gay with blossoms of bird-cherry, gean and hawthorn.* The woodland ground flora is still quite rich and contains wood anemones, wood-sorrel, wild garlic, ground ivy, sweet woodruff, enchanter's nightshade, red campion, wood avens, dog-violets and glorious sheets of bluebells. There is a danger to the latter since although the woodland's plants are predominately our native wild bluebells (*Hyancinthoides non-scripta*) there are non-native Spanish bluebell (*Hyacinthoides hispanica*) garden escapes growing wild all around the Park and these are interbreeding with this native stock.

The botanical gem of these woodlands was the attractive and rare yellow star-of-Bethlehem (Plate 5). Although not originally included in Moyes' list he must have been aware of it. Gilbert McDougall described that it was found *in the bushes near the rifle butts* at an 1882 meeting of Stirling Field and Archeological Club and it was subsequently collected from the site for an exhibition at the Glasgow Natural History Society in 1887. Fear that it would be dug up seems to have led to its location being kept a secret and in David Morris' 1920 account he states *The home of this rare and beautiful plant is well known to a limited circle of nature lovers and the secret will not be lightly given away.* In 1977 Crockart reported an unusually prolific flowering of the colony in the woods now adjacent to the plastic tunnel-houses (NS 7797 9335), the sight reminding him of the scene portrayed in Wordsworth's poem *Daffodils.* Sadly the plant has not been seen for the last ten years, however *Gagea lutea* is an intermittent flowerer and there is still a chance it has been overlooked.

Although there are still places where the dolerite rock breaks through to the surface in the golf course it seems likely that such bare stony ground was much more common in Moyes' time. Cattle and human feet would have kept the rocks free of humus which, if left to accumulate, encourages the growth of coarse grasses and eventually scrub. For instance Moyes describes the flagstaff area on the cliff tops above the rifle butts as being covered in crumbling rock soil with associated tiny plants like common stork's-bill whereas today it is covered in coarse grasses, bracken and scrub. The bare ground shown around the Herd's Hoose in Baker's picture (Plate 4) is now largely gone and is either part of a golf tee or submerged under planted mountain ash, rhododendrons, oak and broom. The 'rocking stone' erratic in the foreground of the picture remains beside the 3rd green. A number of plants that colonise such bare, stony or thinly soiled habitats have been lost including bird's-foot, annual knawell, viper's bugloss, great mullein, restharrow, deadly nightshade, biting stonecrop and cudweed. Some species like English stonecrop and sheep's sorrel remain on rock outcrops and corn spurrey was found surviving in an ancient pile of spent bunker sand. A number of local accounts including Moyes' refer to the *thriving very handsome* clumps of bloody crane's-bill which once lit up the quarries with its beautiful purple-crimson flowers (Plate 5). Perhaps because the quarries stopped working the plant is no longer found there but the multi-coloured colonies of foxgloves which adorn some of the bare rock faces provide attractive substitutes.

What were once Moyes' flower covered grassy slopes and pasture-land have undergone dramatic change over the last century as most of this area has become a tree lined golf course and recreational area. Native broad-leaved plants are so effectively excluded from the fairways and greens that these areas are disparagingly referred to by naturalists as 'green concrete' because they support so little wildlife. Around the periphery of the course above the wooded cliffs there was until recently quite extensive areas of relic short wild flower-rich grassland. After the withdrawal of cattle there was a period when rabbits, deer, human attrition and occasional mowing kept limited areas of this grass short. Today such habitat is restricted to a few picnicking spots and the edges of footpaths and the fairways. The dumping of golf course waste and the growth of nettles, brambles and gorse have reduced the human foot fall which in turn has encouraged the development of extensive tracts of coarse grassland and scrub. An illustration of the scale of this loss is provided by the history of wild yellow and purple pansies (Plate 4). These flowers were once a well-known attraction of the Park being described as *growing in great abundance* by Hutton-Forrest (1821), Nimmo (1880) and Moyes (1908). Numbers have slowly dwindled and the last colony was recorded in May 2007. It seems something of an irony that local garden centres grow and sell large numbers of selected wild pansies which are highly valued to adorn people's gardens. At the same time the natural spectacle provided by probably tens or hundreds of thousands of these plants has been allowed to disappear without a word of protest. Pansies are not the only attractive plants to be lost, the list includes early purple orchid (Plate 5; Moyes, 1908), meadow saxifrage (Nimmo, 1880) and field gentian (Huttons Forrest, 1821). Yellow rattle is considered an essential plant for the maintenance of wildflower rich grassland. It is a parasite on grasses which it dwarfs and consequently allows other short flowering plants to compete. While it has not been located on the golf course area it was found in the fields near the Homesteads and is also being used in the recent wild flower plantings. There are a few short grassland species which remain including the eyebrights, the speedwells, the bedstraws, birds-foot trefoil, and yarrow. Amongst the new grassland species there are a few welcome native acquisitions including the common spotted orchid.

After grazing stopped the coarser grasses took over the meadowlands and much of the golf course rough. Some plants have prospered in these taller grasses including pignut, harebells, knapweed, devil's-bit scabious, bluebells, tormentil, hogweed and ragwort. In turn these areas of coarse grasses are now gradually being overtaken by scrub, different patches being dominated by bracken, rosebay willowherb, elder, brambles, wild raspberries and gorse.

Over the last century very little thought has been given to the conservation of wildlife in King's Park. The woodlands have survived by default rather than by design and sadly we have lost rare species like yellow star-of-Bethlehem and habitats like the wild pansy dominated grassland. Too late we have recognised the importance of such wildflower rich meadowland as a food source for bumble bees. As a consequence to ensure that bees are around to pollinate the apple trees in the newly established King's Park orchard the wild flowers necessary to sustain them have been planted close by. During the past year the Crown Estates have passed the responsibility for the area to Scottish Ministers and they in turn have leased it to Stirling Council for 125 years. It is to be hoped that a proper management plan for the park will be drawn up which includes its wildlife. There is plenty of advice available: Bumblebee Conservation, Plant Life Scotland, Butterfly Conservation Scotland, Buglife Scotland are based in the city, most no more than a five minutes walk away. The Scottish Golf Environment Group who are experts at the design of eco-friendly courses are also keen to be involved.

References

Arthur, J. 2014. Golf Ecology News: Milestones in the Twentieth Century. http://www.golfecology.co.uk/milestones.html

Bowie, J. 2014. Some notes on the history of golf: greenkeeping in the past. http://home.btconnect.com/comestand/FGreen.html

Crockart, I.B. 1977. A note on Yellow Star of Bethlehem. *The Forth Naturalist and Historian* 2, 69-70.

Hutton Forrest, W. 1821. Report, chemical and medical of the Airthrey mineral springs: List of rare and interesting phaenogamous plants collected in the vicinity of Stirling.

Mabey, R. 1996. *Flora Britannica*. Sinclair Stevenson: London.

McDougall, G. 1882. Notes on local plants. *Transactions of Stirling Natural History and Archaeological Society* **5**, 63-67.

Moyes, A. 1908. Notes of the wild plants of King's Park. *Transactions of the Stirling Natural History and Archaeological Society* **30**, 152-175.

Nimmo, W. 1880. *The History of Stirlingshire (3rd Edn).* Thomas D. Morrison: Glasgow.

Preston, C.D., Valtuena, F. J., Kadereit J.W. 2012 The intriguing case of the Welsh poppy *Meconopsis cambrica. British Wildlife* **24**, 16-21.

Appendix

Plants of Kings Park Stirling

Plants from Moyes 1908 list still present in 2014

Common Name	*Latin Name*
Alder	*Alnus glutinosa*
Annual meadow-grass	*Poa annua*
Ash	*Fraxinus excelsior*
Barren strawberry	*Potentilla sterilis*
Bird cherry	*Prunus padus*
Birds-foot trefoil	*Lotus corniculatus*
Bittersweet	*Solanum ducamara*
Blackthorn	*Prunus spinosa*
Bluebell	*Hyacinthoides non-scripta*
Bramble	*Rubus fruticosus agg*
Broad-leaved dock	*Rumex obtusifolius*
Broad-leaved willowherb	*Epilobium montanum*
Brooklime	*Veronica beccabunga*
Broom	*Cytisus scoparius*
Bugle	*Ajuga reptans*
Bulbous buttercup	*Ranunculus bulbosus*
Burdock	*Arctium minus*
Burnet rose	*Rosa pimpernellifolia*
Bush vetch	*Vicia sepium*
Chickweed	*Stellaria media*
Cleavers	*Galium aparine*
Cock's foot	*Dactylis glomerata*
Colt'sfoot	*Tussilago farfara*
Common figwort	*Scrophularia nodosa*
Common mouse-ear	*Cerastium fontanum*
Common sedge	*Carex nigra*
Common sorrel	*Rumex acetosa*
Contoneaster	*Cotoneaster spp*
Corn spurrey	*Spergula arvensis*
Couch grass	*Elytrigia repens*
Cow parsley	*Anthriscus sylvestris*
Creeping buttercup	*Ranunculus repens*
Creeping soft-grass	*Holcus mollis*
Creeping thistle	*Cirsium arvense*
Crested dog's-tail	*Cynosurus cristatus*
Crested hair-grass	*Koeleria macrantha*
Cuckooflower	*Cardamine pratensis*
Curled-dock	*Rumex crispus*
Daisy	*Bellis perennis*
Dandelions	*Taraxacum agg.*
Devil's-bit scabious	*Succisa pratensis*
Dog's mercury	*Mercurialis perennis*
Dog-rose	*Rosa canina*
Dog-violet	*Viola riviniana*
Elder	*Sambucus nigra*
Enchanter's nightshade	*Circaea lutetiana*
English stonecrop	*Sedum anglicum*
Eyebrights	*Euphrasia officinalis*
Field forget-me-not	*Myosotis arvensis*
Field wood-rush	*Luzula campestris*
Foxglove	*Digitalis purpurea*
Gean	*Prunus avium*
Germander speedwell	*Veronica chamaedrys*
Golden saxifrage	*Chrysosplenium oppositifolium*
Gooseberry	*Ribes uva-crispa*
Gorse	*Ulex europaeus*
Great wood-rush	*Luzula sylvatica*
Greater plantain	*Plantago major*
Greater stitchwort	*Stellaria holostea*
Ground ivy	*Glechoma hederacea*
Ground-elder	*Aegopodium podagraria*
Groundsel	*Senecio vulgaris*
Harebell	*Campanula rotundifolia*
Hawkweeds	*Hieracium agg.*
Hawthorn	*Crataegus monogyna*
Hazel	*Corylus avellana*
Heath bedstraw	*Galium saxatile*
Heath speedwell	*Veronica officinalis*
Heath wood-rush	*Luzula multiflora*
Hedge Woundwort	*Stachys sylvatica*
Hemp-nettle	*Galeopsis tetrahit*
Herb-robert	*Geranium robertianum*
Hogweed	*Heracleum sphondylium*
Honeysuckle	*Lonicera periclymenum*
Ivy	*Hedera helix*
Knapweed	*Centaurea nigra*
Lady's bedstraw	*Galium verum*
Lesser trefoil	*Trifolium dubium*
Lesser celandine	*Ranunculus ficaria*
Lesser stitchwort	*Stellaria gaminea*
Marsh cinquefoil	*Potentilla palustris*
Marsh foxtail	*Alopecurus geniculatus*
Marsh marigold	*Caltha palustris*
Marsh thistle	*Cirsium palustre*
Meadow buttercup	*Ranunculus acris*
Meadow foxtail	*Alopecurus pratensis*
Meadowsweet	*Filipendula ulmaria*
Mouse-ear-hawkweed	*Pilosella officinarum*
Nettle	*Urtica dioica*
Nipplewort	*Lapsana communis*
Oxeye daisy	*Leucanthemum vulgare*
Pedunculate oak	*Quercus robor*
Pignut	*Conopodium majus*
Primrose	*Primula vulgaris*
Procumbent pearlwort	*Sagina procumbens*
Ragwort	*Senecio jacobaea*
Ransoms	*Allium ursinum*
Raspberry	*Rubus ideaus*
Red campion	*Silene dioica*
Red clover	*Trifolium pratense*
Ribwort plantain	*Plantago lanceolata*
Rough chervil	*Chaerophyllum temulentum*
Rowan	*Sorbus aucuparia*
Scentless mayweed	*Matricaria recutita*

Sedge green-ribbed	*Carex binervis*
Selfheal	*Prunella vulgaris*
Sheep's -fescue	*Festuca ovina*
Sheep's sorrel	*Rumex acetosella*
Shepherd's-purse	*Capsella bursa-pastoris*
Shining crane's-bill	*Geranium lucidum*
Silverweed	*Potentilla anserina*
Soft rush	*Juncus effusus*
Spear thistle	*Cirsium vulgare*
Sticky mouse-ear	*Cerastium glomeratum*
Sweet woodruff	*Galium odoratum*
Sweet cicely	*Myrrhis odorata*
Sweet vernal-grass	*Anthoxanthum odoratum*
Sycamore	*Acer pseudoplatanus*
Three nerved sandwort	*Moehringia trinervia*
Thyme	*Thymus polytrichus*
Thyme leaved sandwort	*Arenaria serpyllifolia*
Thyme leaved speedwell	*Veronica serpyllifolia*
Tormentil	*Potentilla erecta*
Tufted vetch	*Vicia cracca*
Viper's-bugloss	*Echium vulgare*
Wall speedwell	*Veronica arvensis*
Water blinks	*Montia fontana*
Water cresses	*Rorippa nasturtium aquaticum*
Water forget-me-not	*Myosotis scorpiodes*
White poplar	*Populus alba*
White campion	*Silene latifolia*
White clover	*Trifolium repens*
White dead nettle	*Lamium album*
Whitlow-grasses	*Erophila verna*
Wood anenome	*Anenome nemorosa*
Wood avens	*Geum urbanum*
Wood sage	*Teucrium scorodonia*
Wood-sorrel	*Oxalis acetosella*
Wych elm	*Ulmus glabra*
Yarrow	*Achillea millefolium*
Yellow iris	*Iris pseudacorus*
Yellow vetchling	*Lathyrus pratensis*
Yellow-rattle	*Rhinanthus minor*
Zigzag clover	*Trifolium medium*

Plants in Moyes 1908 list not refound 2014

Agrimony	*Agrimonia eupatoria*
Annual knawel	*Scleranthus annuus*
Annual pearlwort	*Sagina apetala*
Autumn hawkbit	*Leontodon autumnalis*
Bearded couch	*Elymus caninus*
Bilberry	*Vaccinium myrtillus*
Bird's-foot	*Ornithopus perpusillus*
Biting stonecop	*Sedum acre*
Bitter-vetch	*Lathyrus linifolius*
Bloody crane's-bill	*Geranium sanguineum*
Bog stitchwort	*Stellaria uliginosa*
Branched bur-reed	*Sparganium erectum*
Broad-leaved pondweed	*Potamogeton natans*
Burnet saxifrage	*Pimpinella saxifraga*
Carnation sedge	*Carex panicea*
Cat's-ear	*Hypochoeris radicata*
Changing forget-me-not	*Myosotis discolor*
Common milkwort	*Polygala vulgaris*
Crosswort	*Cruciata laevipes*
Cudweed	*Gnaphalium sylvaticum*
Deadly nightshade	*Atropa belladonna*
Doves foot cranes-bill	*Geranium molle*
Duckweed	*Lemna minor*
Eared-willow	*Salix aurita*
Early forget-me-not	*Myosotis ramosissima*
Early hair-grass	*Aira praecox*
Early-purple orchid	*Orchis mascula*
False brome	*Brachypodium sylvaticum*
Fat-hen	*Chenopodium album*
Field madder	*Sherardia arvensis*
Field spurrey	*Spergularia rubra*
Field-speedwell	*Veronica agrestis*
Floating sweet grass	*Glyceria fluitans*
Giant bellflower	*Campanula latifolia*
Goldilocks	*Ranunculus auricomus*
Good-king-henry	*Chenopodium bonus-henricus*
Great mullein	*Verbascum thapsus*
Greater bird's-foot-trefoil	*Lotus pedunculatus*
Hairy buttercup	*Ranunculus sardous*
Hairy sedge	*Carex hirta*
Heath grass	*Danthonia decumbens*
Heath groundsel	*Senecio sylvaticus*
Heath milkwort	*Polygala serpyllifolia*
Heath rush	*Juncus squarrosus*
Ivy-leaved crowfoot	*Ranunculus hederaceus*
Knot grasses	*Polygonum aviculare*
Lady's mantle	*Alchemilla glabra*
Lesser spearwort	*Ranunculus flammula*
Marsh woundwort	*Stachys palustris*
Marsh-bedstraw	*Galium palustre*
Mat-grass	*Nardus stricta*
Mountain pansy	*Viola lutea*
Parsley-piert	*Aphanes arvensis*
Perforate St John's-wort	*Hypericum perforatum*
Prickly sedge	*Carex muricata*
Pyrenean valerian	*Valeriana pyrenaica*
Quaking-grass	*Briza media*
Ragged-robin	*Lychnis flos-cuculi*
Red bartsia	*Odontites vernus*
Restharrow	*Ononis repens*
Sharp-flowered rush	*Juncus acutiflorus*
Slender St John's-wort	*Hypericum pulchrum*
Smith's pepperwort	*Lepidium heterophyllum*
Sneezewort	*Achillea ptarmica*
Spring sedge	*Carex caryophyllea*
Spurge-laurel	*Daphne laureola*
Stork's-bill	*Erodium circutarium*

Sun spurge	*Euphorbia helioscopia*
Tansy	*Tanacetum vulgare*
Thale cress	*Arabidopsis thaliana*
Trailing St John's-wort	*Hypericum humifusum*
Water-plantain	*Alisma plantago-aquatica*
Water-starwort	*Callitriche stagnalis*
Wild basil	*Clinopodium vulgare*
Wild pansy	*Viola tricolor*
Wild strawberry	*Fragaria vesca*
Wood melick	*Melica uniflora*
Wood sanicle	*Sanicula europaea*
Wood stitchwort	*Stellaria nemorum*
Yellow sedge	*Carex flava*
Yellow star-of-Bethlehem	*Gagea lutea*

Species found in 2014 not on Moyes 1908 list

Alsike white-clover	*Trifolium hybridum*
Amercian willowherb	*Epilobium ciliatum*
Apple	*Malus sylvestris*
Aubrietia	*Aubrietia deltoidea*
Beech	*Fagus sylvatica*
Bottle sedge	*Carex rostrata*
Bridlewort	*Spirea salicifolia*
Buddleja	*Buddleja davidii*
Charlock	*Sinapis arvensis*
Cherry laurel	*Prunus laurocerasus*
Climbing corydalis	*Ceratocapnos claviculata*
Common vetch	*Vicia sativa*
Daffodils	*Narcissus agg.*
Darwin's barberry	*Berberis darwinii*
Dotted loosestrife	*Lysimachia punctata*
Downy birch	*Betula pubescens*
Fairy foxglove	*Erinus alpinus*
False oat-grass	*Arrhenatherum elatius*
Field mouse-ear	*Cerastium arvense*
Garden tulips	*Tulipa gesneriana*
Garlic mustard	*Alliaria petiolata*
Giant hogweed	*Heracleum mantegazzianum*
Goat willow	*Salix capea*
Great willowherb	*Epilobium hirsutum*
Greater periwinkle	*Vinca major*
Green alkanet	*Pentaglotis sempervirens*
Hairy bittercress	*Cardamine hirsuta*
Hairy tare	*Vicia hirsuta*
Hedge bindweed	*Calystegia sepium*
Himalayan balsam	*Impatiens glandulifera*
Himalayan cotoneaster	*Cotoneaster simonsii*
Holly	*Ilex aquifolium*
Horse-chestnut	*Aesculus hippocastanum*
Ivy-leaved speedwell	*Veronica hederifolia*
Ivy-leaved toadflax	*Cymbalaria muralis*
Japanese Rose	*Rosa rugosa*
Kidney vetch	*Anthyllis vulneraria*
Lady's mantle (garden)	*Alchemilla mollis*
Larch	*Larix decidua*
Leopard's-bane	*Doronicum pardalianches*
Lesser periwinkle	*Vinca minor*
Leyland cypress	*Cupressocyparis leylandii*
Lilac	*Syringa vulgaris*
Lime	*Tilia x vulgaris*
Little mouse-ear	*Cerastium semidecandrum*
Lords and ladies	*Arum maculatum*
Lungwort	*Pulmonaria officinalis*
Marsh cudweed	*Gnaphilium uliginosum*
Monk's-hood	*Aconitum napellus*
Northern rock-cress	*Arabis petraea*
Norway maple	*Acer platanoides*
Norway spruce	*Picea abies*
Oregon-grape	*Mahonia aquifolium*
Ornamental cherry	*Prunus serrulata*
Ornamental oaks	*Quercus spp.*
Peach-leaved bellflower	*Campanula persicifolia*
Perennial rye-grass	*Lolium perenne*
Pheasant's eye daffodil	*Narcissus poeticus*
Pick-a-back-plant	*Tolmiea menziesii*
Pineappleweed	*Matricaria discoidea*
Pirri-pirri-bur	*Acaena anserinifolia*
Prickly sow thistle	*Sonchus asper*
Red currant	*Ribes rubrum*
Red fescues	*Festuca rubra*
Red horse-chestnut	*Aesculus carnea*
Rhododendron	*Rhododendron ponticum*
Rock crane's-bill	*Geranium macrorrhizum*
Rosebay willowherb	*Chamerion angustifolium*
Rough meadow-grass	*Poa trivialis*
Scentless mayweed	*Tripleurospermum inodorum*
Scots pine	*Pinus sylvestris*
Sessile oak	*Quercus petraea*
Silver birch	*Betula pendula*
Sitka spruce	*Picea sitchensis*
Slender parsley-piert	*Aphanes australis*
Smooth sow-thistle	*Sonchus oleraceus*
Snowberry	*Symphoricarpos albus*
Snowdrop	*Galanthus nivalis*
Soft-brome	*Bromus hordeaceus*
Solomon's seal	*Polygonatum multiflorum*
Spanish bluebell	*Hyacinthoides hispanica*
Tuberous comfrey	*Symphytum tuberosum*
Tutsan	*Hypericum androsaemum*
Upright hedge-parsley	*Torilis japonica*
Wall cotoneaster	*Cotoneaster horizontalis*

Wavy bitter-cress	*Cardamine flexuosa*
Wavy hair-grass	*Deschampsia flexuosa*
Welsh poppy	*Meconopsis cambrica*
Whitebeam	*Sorbus aria*
Winter-cress	*Barbarea vulgaris*
Wood speedwell	*Veronica montana*
Wood-sedge	*Carex sylvatica*
Yellow corydalis	*Pseudofumaria lutea*
Yorkshire-fog	*Holcus lanatus*

Notes

Moyes (1908) latin names were changed to modern counterparts using Clapham, Tutin and Warburg's *Flora of the British Isles* 2nd Edition 1958 as an intermediary.

The listed common and latin names are those used in the *New Atlas of the Britsh and Irish Flora* 2002.

Gagea lutea was added to Moyes' list because its location was being kept a secret.

ROOKERIES IN THE UPPER FORTH BIRD RECORDING AREA

Neil Bielby

(Bird recording in Scotland is organised and monitored by the Scottish Ornithologists' Club (SOC). The Upper Forth is one of 20 areas into which Scotland is divided for this purpose and covers the Clackmannanshire, Falkirk and Stirling Council areas excluding that part of the latter which drains into the Clyde).

Introduction

The familiar Rook (*Corvus frugilegus*) is a large, common, resident corvid which nests communally – often close to human habitation. It mostly inhabits lowland agricultural and suburban areas where it finds its diet of mainly invertebrates and cereal grains but does forage some upland habitats in summer where crane-flies are the main food source. The large, mature trees preferred for nesting colonies are plentiful throughout the Upper Forth area and this, along with a suitable mixture of grazed and arable farmland, means that this species is well represented here.

Fluctuations in Rook numbers can be monitored in several ways e.g. Breeding Bird Survey (BBS) transects or by either local or national bird atlas work but the favoured (and arguably most effective) way is to count the number of rookeries and nests within them. This is facilitated by the fact that Rooks breed early in the year and are incubating eggs by late March/early April, before leaf cover develops, making the nests visible from some distance – especially if on the skyline.

Rookeries are located using one of two methods – either prior knowledge or the 'look-see' method when covering an area – usually by vehicle. These methods normally account for most of the rookeries present in an area although experience has shown that the odd one, usually in conifers or hidden by the lie of the land and often only accessible by private road, is missed.

The first known full survey of rookeries in the Upper Forth area was carried out in the spring of 1975 as part of a nationwide survey organised by the British Trust for Ornithology (BTO). Subsequently, sporadic counts of some well known rookeries have been undertaken and published in the local bird reports from 1976 up to the present. Additionally, comprehensive counts were undertaken in Stirling District (the author 1997 and by Douglas Kerr and Dr. Chris Spray 2008); Clackmannanshire (the author 1998 and 2102) and Falkirk District (the author 2001 and 2014).

This paper lists and attempts to interpret the findings of these surveys.

Results

The total number of nests recorded is shown in Table1 with the total number of rookeries shown in Table 2 (average number of nests per rookery in brackets).

Table 1.

Year	1975	1997 - 2001	2008 - 2014
Clackmannanshire	544	942	758
Falkirk District	2072	2598	1097
Stirling District	1497	2186	2965
Totals	4113	5726	4820

Table 2.

Year	1975	1997 - 2001	2008 - 2014
Clackmannanshire	14 (39)	20 (47)	25 (30)
Falkirk District	32 (65)	65 (40)	49 (22)
Stirling District	46 (33)	76 (29)	93 (32)
Totals	92 (45)	161 (36)	167 (29)

Details of individual rookeries can be found in the appendices. A photograph of a typical rookery can be found on plate 6.

Population changes

As the tables above illustrate while the overall number of nests in the Upper Forth has fluctuated the number of rookeries has increased quite steadily since the 1975 baseline. This has led to a decrease in the average number of nests per rookery.

Breaking the results down into the three council areas; Clackmannanshire and Falkirk followed a similar pattern of an apparent increase in both the number of rookeries (43 % and 103 %) and nests (73 % and 25 %) between 1975 and around the turn of the century. Since then the number of nests has declined by 20 % and 58 % in Clackmannanshire and Falkirk Council respectively. By contrast, both the number of rookeries and nests in the Stirling council area increased by 62 % and 40 % in the first period and by a further 22 % and 36 % in the second period.

Although there is probably an unknown and differing degree of surveyor effort/bias at work the survey methods are quite straightforward and with the same surveyor carrying out some of the repeat council area surveys this means that the figures should be reasonably robust.

Therefore, assuming that the results are largely indicative of the true trends, the reasons for the quite noticeable changes both within and between the different council areas are not readily explained. Varying availability of food is the most likely cause although persecution cannot be ruled out and may have a localised effect (although Rooks aid the farmer by eating land based invertebrates they can also be considered a pest by both eating newly sown cereal seeds and in damaging young plants as they forage and can be shot by landowners under licence).

To put these findings in a wider context, the 1996 BTO census (surveying random km squares rather than a total count) suggested an increase of 39 % in the number of nests between 1975-1996, a rise of 1.9 % per annum. During a slightly longer period the Upper Forth showed a similar increase of 1.7 % p.a. The increases for the three local districts during this period were: Clackmannanshire 3.2 % p.a.; Falkirk 1.0 % p.a. and Stirling 1.8 % p.a. Since 1996, local surveys suggest an increase of 3.7 % p.a. in the Stirling council area compared to decreases of 1.8 % p.a. in Clackmannanshire and 4.5% p.a. in Falkirk.

There has been no dedicated UK rookery survey since 1996 but the BTO's annual monitoring scheme (BBS) indicates a statistically significant decline of 34 % between 1995-2011 which equates to 2.1 % p.a. (Risely et al 2013).

Site fidelity

BWP (Cramp *et al* 1977-1994) states that *fidelity to colony and nest site generally high* so it comes as something of a surprise to find that only 47 % of the rookeries found in the Upper Forth area were still extant around the year 2000 (Clackmannanshire 33 %; Falkirk 47 % and Stirling 59 %).This trend has continued over the past 10-15 years with 63 % surviving this period (Clackmannanshire 62 %; Falkirk 55 % and Stirling 69 %). The latter set of figures being quite consistent. In total, only 40 % of the rookeries counted in the Upper Forth area in 1975 were still active c.36 years later.

Density

This is probably best expressed as nests per km$^{2.}$ The BTO 1975 survey gave a Scottish average of 3.2 (surprisingly only 0.7 lower than the English average of 3.9). The local densities were: Clackmannanshire 3.4, Falkirk 7.0 and Stirling 0.9. These differing densities probably reflecting the mix of upland and lowland in the three council areas. Densities from the most recent surveys are: Clackmannanshire 4.7; Falkirk 3.7 and Stirling 1.7. The highest density in Britain was recorded in the Ythan Valley NE Scotland at 24 nests per km^2 (Dunnet *et al*. 1968).

Colony size

The average number of nests per colony in the most recent surveys (1975 averages in brackets) were: Clackmannanshire 22.7 (38.9); Falkirk 11.8 (64.8) and Stirling 31.9 (32.6). This shows that the number of nests per colony in the Falkirk Council area has fallen even more markedly than the total number of nests. By contrast, the increase in the overall number of nests in the Stirling Council area appears to be due to new colonies being formed rather than existing ones expanding. In Clackmannanshire the number of colonies has almost doubled since 1975 but the new ones hold fewer nests with a corresponding decrease in the average colony size. In 1975 the average number of nests per colony in Scotland was 79.1 with the largest colony, Hatton Castle Complex, Grampian, containing 2,669 nests. North-east Scotland has the highest densities and largest colonies in Britain and probably Europe. (Forrester and Andrews 2007)

Colony trees

Forrester and Andrews (2007) state that in Scotland most nests are in conifers – mainly Scots Pine. However, for the 61 rookeries (37 %) in the Upper Forth area where the nesting trees were recorded, 61 % were in deciduous, 13 % in conifers (mostly Scots Pine) and 26 % in mixed conifer/deciduous.

Altitude

Colonies in the Upper Forth area occur from sea level up to 210 m (Buckieburn, NS 755857).

Conclusions

The total of 4607 nests (and therefore breeding pairs) from the latest surveys indicate an increase of 12 % from the 1975 survey – but a fall of 21 % from the surveys carried out around the turn of the 20th/21st centuries. This hints at considerable fluidity in not only the number of nests but also the number, size and location of colonies. This suggests that annual counts of randomly selected large colonies are unlikely to give a true reflection of Rook population dynamics throughout an area.

References:

Cramp, S. and Perrins, C.M. (eds). 1994. *The Birds of the Western Palearctic.* Vol. 8. Oxford, Oxford University Press.

Dunnet, G.M. and Patterson, I.J. 1968. The Rook problem in north-east Scotland. In Murton, R.K. and Wright, E. N. (eds) *The Problems of Birds as Pests.* pp 119-139, London, Academic Press.

Forrester, R.W. and Andrews, I.J. *et al* (eds) 2007. *The Birds of Scotland* Aberlady, The Scottish Ornithologists' Club.

Risely, K. *et al.* 2013. *The Breeding Bird Survey 2012.* BTO Research Report 645. Thetford, British Trust for Ornithology.

Appendix 1 Clackmannanshire rookeries

Location	Grid Ref	Date	Nests	Date	Nests	Date	Nests
	NN 80	**1975**		**1998**		**2012**	
Easter Cornhill	NN 978000			15.3.98	35	1.4.12	33
	NS 89						
Main St W., Menstrie	NS 845970	1.4.75	136	13.4.98	126	4.4.12	159
Windsor St., Menstrie	NS 845968			13.4.98	17	4.4.12	3
Distillery Brae	NS 856943	?.3.75	20				
A907 at Cambus	NS 858941					1.4.12	69
Menstrie Maltings	NS 858965	30.4.75	32			4.4.12	16
Myreton	NS 858974			16.4.98	50	4.4.12	25
Orchard Farm	NS 860933			14.4.98	21	1.4.12	78
Dams, Menstrie	NS 862970			16.4.98	55	4.4.12	0
Alloa W.	NS 874930			8.4.98	103	1.4.12	73
Gean House (a), Alloa	NS 875938			8.4.98	45	1.4.12	30
Gean House (b), Alloa	NS 875941					6.4.12	6
Cochrane Park, Alva	NS 876970					1.4.12	37
Comely Bank, Alloa	NS 892927			14.4.98	13	1.4.12	46
Keilarsbrae, Alloa	NS 894938	1.4.75	120			1.4.12	2
Hallpark, Alloa	NS 895936			20.4.04	51	1.4.12	0
	NS 99						
Mary Br, Clackmannan Town	NS 909923					1.4.12	13
Chapelhill, Clackmannan Town	NS 913914					1.4.12	15
Riccarton, Clackmannan	NS 913921	27.4.75	45	14.4.98	58	1.4.12	34
W. of Devonside	NS 913972	19.4.75	5				
Gartmorn Dam	NS 917942	27.4.75	7	16.4.98	154	1.4.12	0
Devonside	NS 923960					4.4.12	11
Tillicoultry	NS 922969	19.4.75	12				
Cunninghar, Tillicoultry	NS 924977			14.4.98	12	1.4.12	36
Harviestoun Burn	NS 931971			13.4.98	54	1.4.12	0
Harviestoun Mine	NS 938976			13.4.98	12	1.4.12	0
East Lodge Burn	NS 943980			13.4.98	12	1.4.12	0
Dollarbank	NS 944982					1.4.12	20
Aberdona House	NS 945950	27.4.75	72	14.4.98	63	4.4.12	2
Belmont, Dollar W.	NS 947976			13.4.98	19	1.4.12	19
R. Devon at Broomrigg	NS 948977	13.4.75	5				
Broomrigg, Dollar	NS 948979	12.4.75	12				
A 91 (Broomrigg-Dollar)	NS 952979			13.4.98	9	1.4.12	0
Bryanstone Drive, Dollar	NS 954978			13.4.98	4	1.4.12	0
Dollar Acadamey	NS 961981	12.4.75	4				
Kellybank	NS 970984					1.4.12	9
Dollarbeg	NS 971963	20.4.75	21	15.3.98	29		
Woodside Farm	NS 975948					1.4.12	7
Cadger Burn, Solsgirth	NS 981959	20.4.75	53				
Shelterhall	NS 985984					1.4.12	13
Muchart Mill	NS 992986					15.3.05	2
	Nests		**544**		**942**		**758**
	Rookeries		**14**		**20**		**25**

No subsequent entry/data for rookeries counted in 1975 does not necessarily mean that these sites weren't checked in the following two surveys.

Appendix 2 Falkirk rookeries

Location	Grid Ref	Date	Nests	Date	Nests	Date	Nests
	NS 77	1975		2001		2014	
Glenskirlie House, Banknock	NS 776791			17.4.01	25	15.4.14	28
	NS 78						
Nicolswalls (Riverside Fm)	NS 763842					15.4.14	5
Grayswalls	NS 767842					15.4.14	3
Langhill	NS 769841					15.4.14	10
Meadowgreens	NS 772827			17.4.01	27	15.4.14	16
Overton	NS 772835			17.4.01	23	15.4.14	0
Hookney	NS 775837	26.4.75	32	17.4.01	19	15.4.14	0
Northshields	NS 775839			17.4.01	5	15.4.14	0
Braeface	NS 783800			17.4.01	18	15.4.14	23
Stoneywood	NS 798829					15.4.14	48
	NS 87						
Woodend Farm, Allandale	NS 800785	26.4.75	68	17.4.01	23	15.4.14	14
Castlecary brickworks	NS 803786	24.4.75	62	17.4.01	0	15.4.14	0
Underwood House	NS 804790			17.4.01	26	15.4.14	0
Lochgreen	NS 817772			17.4.01	22	15.4.14	0
Bonnyside House	NS 834798			17.4.01	32	15.4.14	68
N. of Southfield, Slamannan	NS 840721	19.4.75	93	18.4.01	89	14.4.14	43
Southfield Fm	NS 842720					14.4.14	19
Slamannan	NS 856730					14.4.14	93
Balquhatstone House. Slamannan.	NS 858725	19.4.75	70	18.4.01	76	14.4.14	3
B816 W of Falkirk (Tamfourhill)	NS 857798	17.4.75	34	17.4.01	57	15.4.14	36
Camelon	NS 862798	24.4.75	30	17.4.01	0	15.4.14	0
Summerford, Falkirk	NS 867798	26.4.75	16	17.4.01	45	15.4.14	24
Glen Burn	NS 872782			17.4.01	38	15.4.14	0
Crossburn	NS 873728			18.4.01	15	14.4.14	0
Lochend	NS 879748					14.4.14	3
Princess Park, Prospect Hill	NS 881787			17.4.01	36	15.4.14	29
Falkirk Royal Inf.	NS 883797	24.4.75	23	17.4.01	0	15.4.14	0
Union Canal, Glen Village (a)	NS 883783			17.4.01	20	15.4.14	0
Glen Village	NS 883789	26.4.75	11	17.4.01	0	15.4.14	0
Glen Ellrig	NS 884744	21.4.75	549	18.4.01	62	15.4.14	0
Glen Ellrig (a)	NS 883741			18.4.01	97	15.4.14	0
Glen Ellrig (b)	NS 884740			18.4.01	127	15.4.14	0
Dykehead	NS 885719			18.4.01	60	14.4.14	31
Union Canal, Glen Village (b)	NS 886781			17.4.01	51	15.4.14	27
Lower Boxton	NS 888740			18.4.01	61	14.4.14	0
South Bankhead	NS 891731			18.4.01	24	14.4.14	0
North Bankhead (a)	NS 892733			18.4.01	25	14.4.14	0
Babbithill	NS 893722					14.4.14	16
Boagstown (a)	NS 896740			18.4.01	11	14.4.14	0
North Bankhead (b)	NS 894735			18.4.01	6	14.4.14	0
Boagstown (b)	NS 896740			18.4.01	52	14.4.14	0
1 mile W of Denny (Stoneywood)	NS 801828	24.4.75	32	18.4.01	105	15.4.14	0
By M80 (Quarter House)	NS 806846	26.3.75	10	17.4.01	24	15.4.14	20
Rosebank, Dunipace	NS 807837					15.4.14	4
Easterton	NS 808856			17.4.01	14	15.4.14	48

Location	Grid Ref	Date	Nests	Date	Nests	Date	Nests
	NS 88 cont.	1975		2001		2014	
Denny Mill (Dunipace)	NS 809832	26.3.75	22	17.4.01	10	15.4.14	30
Dennyloanhead	NS 809802	24.4.75	27	18.4.01	25	15.4.14	39
Larbert Rd, Bonnybridge	NS 819805			17.4.01	17	15.4.14	11
Headswood, junc 1 M876	NS 829819			17.4.01	12	15.4.14	0
Bonnybridge	NS 831804			17.4.01	15	15.4.14	2
Torwood	NS 842850	27.4.75	34	17.4.01	0	15.4.14	7
Torwood	NS 842853	27.4.75	10	17.4.01	0	15.4.14	0
Torwood	NS 844849			17.4.01	40	15.4.14	3
Wallacebank Wood	NS 847848			17.4.01	125	15.4.14	?
Larbert House Hosp. (b)	NS 849827	24.4.75	112	17.4.01	9	15.4.14	0
Larbert House Hosp. (a)	NS 850827			17.4.01	24	15.4.14	0
Larbert House Hosp. (c)	NS 850826			17.4.01	7	15.4.14	0
Larbert House Hosp. (d)	NS 850830					15.4.14	31
Bellsdyke Hosp (a)	NS 852833	24.4.75	37	17.4.01	0	15.4.14	0
Bellsdyke Hosp (b)	NS 852829	24.4.75	35	17.4.01	0	15.4.14	0
Tamfourhill	NS 855800			17.4.01	20	15.4.14	0
Royal Scottish Nat. Hosp.	NS 857837	24.4.75	9	17.4.01	0	15.4.14	0
Bellsdyke Hosp	NS 866838			17.4.01	33	15.4.14	0
Bellsdyke Rd, Antonhill	NS 874840					15.4.14	2
Dunmore W.	NS 878893			5.4.01	18	14.4.14	0
Kinnaird Lodge	NS 879842			5.4.01	6	14.4.14	0
Junc. 7, M9	NS 889847			5.4.01	11	14.4.14	7
Cuttyfield	NS 891840			5.4.01	18	14.4.14	0
Pinapple NTS, N of Airth	NS 890885	24.4.75	75	5.4.01	174	14.4.14	12
Letham S.	NS 892858	24.4.75	17	5.4.01	0	14.4.14	0
Letham N.	NS 896864	28.4.75	94	5.4.01	0	14.4.14	0
Carron House	NS 897831			17.4.01	10	14.4.14	30
Airth	NS 898872	28.4.75	11			14.4.14	0
Righead	NS 900744					14.4.14	6
Parkhead	NS 915733			18.4.01	15	14.4.14	56
HMP Brightons	NS 921779			17.4.01	22	15.4.14	0
Harlow Grange, Brightons	NS 921781			17.4.01	12	15.4.14	2
Polworth Av., Brightons	NS 924779			17.4.01	10	15.4.14	7
Standburn	NS 930746			18.4.01	13	14.4.14	0
Polmont	NS 930783			17.4.01	2	15.4.14	0
Candie House	NS 935742			18.4.01	20	14.4.14	33
Old Polmont	NS 935787	24.4.75	14	17.4.01	0	15.4.14	0
Tarduff House	NS 948755			18.4.01	57	14.4.14	2
Muiravonside	NS 949755			18.4.01	188	14.4.14	40
	NS 98						
Skinflats Village	NS 908832	9.4.75	2	5.4.01	0	14.4.14	0
Bothkennar	NS 908837	27.3.75	9	5.4.01	0	14.4.14	0
Airth Castle	NS 901870	28.4.75	331	5.4.01	0	14.4.14	0
Haughs of Airth	NS 911861					14.4.14	16
Greendyke	NS 912859					14.4.14	11
Grange Manor, Glensburgh	NS 913816	27.3.75	20	5.4.01	53	14.4.14	11
Powfoulis Hotel	NS 918856	27.3.75	35	5.4.01	102	14.4.14	21

Appendix 2 Falkirk rookeries cont.

Location	Grid Ref	Date	Nests	Date	Nests	Date	Nests
	NS 98 cont.	**1975**		**2001**		**2014**	
North Haining, Grangemouth	NS 960800	20.3.75	148	5.4.01	104	15.4.14	42
Junc A993/A706, Bo'ness	NS 996810			5.4.01	2	14.4.14	0
	NT 07						
Harbour Rd, Bo'ness	NT 011811			6.4.01	74	14.4.14	20
Bridgeness Rd, Bo'ness	NT 018814					14.4.14	2
Blackness	NT 051799			6.4.01	60	14.4.14	71
Totals	**Nests**		**2072**		**2598**		**1097**
	Rookeries		**32**		**65**		**49**
No subsequent entry/data for rookeries counted in 1975 does not necessarily mean that these sites weren't checked in the following two surveys.							

Appendix 3 Stirling rookeries

Location	Grid Ref	Date	Nests	Date	Nests	Date	Nests
	NS 58	**1975**		**1997**		**2008**	
A811, Balfunning	NS 512895					25.4.08	92
	NS 59						
Boreland Ho, Dalmary	NS 516960	11.5.75	36				
A81, Gartartan Fm	NS 533984					25.4.08	26
A 811, Glenfoot	NS 529905			7.4.97	8	25.4.08	0
A 81, Douchlage	NS 534923			7.4.97	48	25.4.08	60
A811, Kepculloch	NS 540918					23.4.08	10
B 835, Gartinstarry	NS 553938	27.4.75	10				
A 811, Craighead	NS 557929			7.4.97	5	23.4.08	0
B 835, Gartbawn	NS 560940	27.4.75	33	7.4.97	46	30.4.08	21
A 811, Cashley Bridge	NS 567933	27.4.75	80	7.4.97	173	23.4.08	118
A811, Buchlyvie	NS 577938					23.4.08	8
B 8034, Goodie Water	NS 595995	27.4.75	38	7.4.97	50	25.4.08	19
	NS69						
Arngibbon Burn	NS 605948	4.5.75	27				
Thorntree	NS 611935	3.5.75	5				
A 811, Arnprior E.	NS 617951	27.4.75	39	7.4.97	3	4.5.08	50
0.8km NE of Arnprior	NS 619955	27.4.75	25				
Kippen Cemetery	NS 635952			7.4.97	4	23.4.08	0
Arngomery, Kippen	NS 639948	22.4.75	52	7.4.97	15	23.4.08	13
Arngomery, High Wood	NS 640943			5.4.97	?		
Arngomery Burn	NS 641948	26.4.75	54				
Kippen W.	NS 646949	22.4.75	15	7.4.97	79	23.4.08	20
Burnside, Kippen	NS 653956					20.4.08	8
Thornhill	NS 668996			11.4.97	5	28.4.08	12
East Murdieston	NS 674987			11.4.97	72	2.5.08	23
A811, Mains of Boquhan	NS 676954					25.4.08	31
Ballinton	NS 680983			11.4.97	15	2.5.08	0
Craighead	NS 685981	22.4.75	31	11.4.97	0		
B 8031, Craighead	NS 691980	22.4.75	17	11.4.97	68	1.5.08	0
Watson Ho	NS 692945	1.5.75	115			9.5.11	41
B 8031, Coldoch Broch	NS 696981			11.4.97	66	24.4.08	4
Bield Farm, Gargunnock	NS 699944			11.4.97	14	25.4.08	0
	NS 78						
Easter Buckieburn	NS 755857					24.4.08	51
Old Sauchie	NS 774885			11.4.97	24	24.4.08	0
Howlands	NS 786894			11.4.97	17	25.4.08	0
	NS 79						
Gargunnock	NS 706943	17.4.75	7	11.4.97	33	25.4.08	62
Gargunnock NE	NS 707945	17.4.75	7				
Gargunnock E.	NS 710943			11.4.97	2	25.4.08	0
Blairdrummond School	NS 718989			11.4.97	25	24.4.08	37
Boreland Hill	NS 718994	26.4.75	26	11.4.97	0		
Cuthill Brae	NS 720992			11.4.97	13	24.4.08	0
Meiklewood	NS 724955	23.4.08	51	17.3.98	37	27.4.08	0
R. Forth, W. Carse Fm	NS 733937	12.4.75	37	11.4.97	0		
Blairdrummond Safari Park	NS 733986					23.4.08	5

Appendix 3 Stirling rookeries cont.

Location	Grid Ref	Date	Nests	Date	Nests	Date	Nests
	NS 79 cont.	1975		1997		2008	
A811, West Carse	NS 738943					28.4.08	25
Ochtertyre Rd	NS 748973					23.4.08	5
A 84, Carrat	NS 752969			11.4.97	16	24.4.08	8
Dripend	NS 753963			11.4.97	25	26.4.08	22
S end Craigforth?	NS 774943	12.4.75	43	11.4.97	0		
Craigforth	NS 774948			11.4.97	171	3.5.08	169
Cambusbarron	NS 779922	17.4.75	24	11.4.97	34	25.4.08	34
Polmaise Home Farm	NS 782920			11.4.97	6	25.4.08	0
King's Park Farm	NS 785935			20.4.97	4	26.4.08	5
Torbrex	NS 787919	17.4.75	22	N/C	N/C	26.4.08	12
Kings Park play area	NS 789928	17.4.75	5	17.4.01	0		
Queen's Rd. Stirling	NS 789932			17.4.01	5	15.4.08	3
Fountain Rd, Br of Allan	NS 790971			17.4.01	5	3.5.08	0
The Bridge of Allan	NS 791976			20.3.97	22	3.5.08	74
Glebe Av. Stirling	NS 793931	17.4.75	2	24.4.97	4	25.4.08	0
Beechwood Ho, Stirling	NS 793920			15.4.97	13	25.4.08	6
Glebe Cres. Stirling	NS 794930			24.4.97	5	25.4.08	6
SRI area	NS 795921	17.4.75	24	24.4.97	0	N/C	N/C
Allan Park, Stirling	NS 796930	17.4.75	10	17.4.97	7	25.4.08	0
	NS 88						
Avenue Wood	NS 805875			11.4.97	2	26.4.08	52
Croftsidepark	NS 807881			15.4.97	26	26.4.08	54
Corbiewood Stadium	NS 808894					30.4.08	30
Plean Country Park	NS 835864			17.4.01	9	26.4.08	0
Cushan Quarter, Plean	NS 838867			15.4.97	34	26.4.08	26
	NS 89						
Balquhidderock Wood	NS 807911			11.4.97	61	26.4.08	340
Meadowpark, Br of Allan	NS 801967	20.4.75	87	20.3.97	98	3.5.08	142
Witches Craig, Blairlogie	NS 820966			26.3.98	11	26.4.08	58
Powis House	NS 823955			26.3.98	7	26.4.08	0
Manorneuk	NS 826950			19.3.97	3	26.4.08	0
Poppletrees Br., Throsk	NS 860910			15.4.97	16	26.4.08	18
Throsk	NS 853914			15.4.97	111	26.4.08	290
	NN 50						
Coille-don, Lake of Menteith	NN 572009	24.4.75	93	21.3.97	38	4.5.08	0
A873 nr Rhinaclach	NN 598015					28.4.08	16
Auchyle, Port of Menteith	NN 596016			19.3.97	4	28.4.08	0
	NN 53						
Killin	NN 571324	13.4.75	22				
	NN 60						
Letter Hill	NN 601044	24.4.75	15				
Ballabeg, A 81	NN 605021			19.3.97	16	28.4.08	44
A873, Blairinhoyle	NN 612012					30.4.08	9
Quarry Wood, Calziemuck	NN 620057			21.3.97	28	11.5.08	0
Ruskie	NN 625008	15.4.75	12				
Easter Lennieston	NN 626014			21.3.97	4	11.5.08	5
Callander	NN 632074			7.4.97	34	20.4.14	99

Location	Grid Ref	Date	Nests	Date	Nests	Date	Nests
	NS 60 cont.	**1975**		**1997**		**2008**	
A873, Wester Boreland	NN 639008			21.3.97	8	8.4.08	29
Torrie	NN 640053	26.4.75	108			10.5.08	44
Gart House	NN 642066			7.4.97	28	20.4.08	0
Gart Farm	NN 643065			7.4.97	7	20.4.08	11
Braendam House	NN 649020	3.5.75	55	11.4.97	26	11.5.08	33
A837, Mollan, W of Thornhill	NN 651005	15.4.75	43	21.3.97	33	28.4.08	63
N of B8032 at Daldorn	NN 671039	26.4.75	7				
Drumvaich Wood	NN 672045	9.4.75	16	21.3.97	81	10.5.08	11
Drumvaich S	NN 672041	09.4.75	24	25.4.97	6	10.5.08	0
Drumvaich N	NN 673043	9.4.75	22	21.3.97	9	20.4.08	6
Mains of Broich Farm	NN 693019			14.4.97	31	30.4.08	12
Lanrick Lodge	NN 695021	26.4.75	15				
	NN 63						
Ardeonaig, L. Tay	NN 668358	26.5.75	21	24.2.02	8	5.5.08	20
	NN 70						
Burn of Cambus	NN 706028			21.3.97	7	20.4.08	3
B826, Causewayend	NN 710008	26.4.75	36				
Deanston 1	NN 710019			14.4.97	5	10.5.08	0
Buchany W	NN 710028			19.3.97	5	20.4.08	0
Buchany E	NN 712028			19.3.97	7	20.4.08	29
Deanston 2	NN 713017			14.4.97	16	8.4.08	27
Creity Hall, Deanston	NN 719009					25.4.08	15
Wood of Doune	NN 724015			18.4.97	23	8.4.08	45
Byrehill, Doune	NN 729014			14.4.97	30	20.4.08	23
Doune Castle	NN 730012	9.4.75	15	14.4.97	8	20.4.08	30
A820 Dunblane-Doune	NN 744010	2.5.75	17				
Strathmore Av. Dunblane	NN 775016			16.4.01	39	14.4.08	27
Railway Station, Dunblane	NN 782010	18.4.75	31	20.3.97	25	17.4.08	18
Holme Hill, Dunblane	NN 783015			27.4.98	122	17.4.08	95
QV School, Dunblane	NN 788028	9.4.75	8	23.3.97	21	14.4.08	66
Ledcameroch	NN 789020	9.4.75	15				
Ochiltree / Kellie Wynd	NN 791022					14.4.08	95
Number of Nests			**1497**		**2186**		**2965**
Number of rookeries			**46**		**76**		**93**

No subsequent entry/data for rookeries counted in 1975 does not necessarily mean that these sites weren't checked in the following two surveys.

2012 AND 2013 MOTH RECORDS FOR STIRLINGSHIRE AND WEST PERTHSHIRE

John T. Knowler

This report constitutes the third update for Stirlingshire and West Perthshire (vice counties 86 and 87) of the data presented in the *Annotated Checklist of the Larger Moths of Stirlingshire, West Perthshire and Dunbartonshire* (Knowler, 2010)

The vice counties 86 and 87

Because they are roughly equal in size and their boundaries have been stable for over a hundred years, the 112 Watsonian vice counties devised by Hewett Cottrell Watson have become a basis for biological recording in the UK. Modern Stirlingshire is roughly split between vice counties 86 and 87. Vice County 86 includes the local authority area of Falkirk and also encompasses areas of modern East Dunbartonshire west to parts of Milngavie and Mugdock Country Park. Vice County 87 includes the western ends of what historically were the counties Clackmannanshire (now part of Fife) and Perthshire.

The effect of weather on the moth assemblage of the region

By common consent, the very wet summer of 2012 was bad for moths across the UK and this was certainly reflected in both the qualitative and the quantitative records from recorders across our region. The weather in 2013 was characterised by a cold spring but when summer finally arrived it proved to be unusually long and clement. This again was reflected in the moth assemblage. Thus, common early spring moths such as those of the genus *Orthosia* were unusually scarce and other early spring species were not recorded. For instance, the author is not aware of any 2013 records for lunar marbled brown (*Drymonia ruficornis*) which is normally not uncommon in April and early May in wooded areas from Loch Lomondside to as far east as Bridge of Allan. Conversely, the closely related but later flying, marbled brown (*Drymonia dodonaea*) was on the wing later in June than usual but if anything was more abundant than in most years. This delayed emergence characterised the flight period of many spring and early summer moths but was not apparent later in the summer and double brooded species like common carpet (*Epirrhoe alternata*) and purple bar (*Cosmorhoe ocellata*) appeared to have particularly strong second broods.

The beautiful snout

In April 2013, David Smith, an inexperienced moth enthusiast, informed the author that on 27th May, 2012 he had found a beautiful snout (*Hypena crassalis*) on the north bank of The Narrows between the two parts of Loch Ard near

Aberfoyle in the Trossachs. Given that the species had never been recorded north of Cumbria, the record seemed most unlikely but it was supported by an excellent, dated photograph (Plate 1a) and clear recollection of the site of discovery. Furthermore, the site was typical habitat, namely closed, mainly oak (*Quercus sp.*) woodland with considerable bilberry (*Vaccinium myrtillus*), the foodplant of beautiful snout, in the understory.

Clearly the discovery required further investigation and it appeared prudent to delay reporting its discovery in central Scotland until its presence as a resident could be confirmed. Thus, from early June 2013, Arthur and Jane Jones, initially accompanied by the author, ran UV light traps at and near the site of the 2012 record. Early attempts failed but Arthur and Jane persisted and on 21st June they caught six beautiful snout on the opposite bank of the Narrows of Loch Ard. On 7th of July they caught another in their garden above the eastern end of the loch. Thus, it is clear that the beautiful snout has established itself in at least one area of the Trossachs but it remains to be seen how widely it has spread.

The normal range of the moth in the UK is mainly southern England, through Wales and in western England as far north as Cumbria (Heath, and Maitland Emmet, 1983). Nevertheless, the species does appear to be becoming more widespread in the north of its range (Hill *et al.*, 2010). The species was new to Lancashire in 2001, was not recorded for a second time until 2007 but is now known from nine separate locations in the county. (S. Palmer, pers. comm..). It was first recorded in Northumberland in 2010 (T. Tams, pers. Comm..). Nevertheless, the beautiful snout has arrived in central Scotland without being first recorded in the south of the country.

Other recent arrivals in the region

The beautiful snout adds to a substantial list of moth species that have moved north into central Scotland perhaps in response to climatic change (Knowler, 2011a). Since 2000 the list has included red-necked footman (*Atolmis rubricollis*) (Knowler, and Mitchell, 2004), slender brindle (*Apamea scolopacina*) (Knowler, 2005), the micro *Ypsolopha sequella*, alder moth (*Acronicta alni*), copper underwing (*Amphipyra pyramidea*), oak-tree pug (*Eupithecia dodoneata*), Blair's shoulder-knot (*Lithophane leautieri*), pale pinion (*Lithophane hepatica*) (Leverton and Palmer, 2009), buff footman (*Eilema depressa*) (Knowler, 2011b), beautiful snout and perhaps lesser treble-bar (*Aplocera plagiata*) although this species may have been previously overlooked. Of these recent arrivals, records from across the region indicate that *Ypsolopha sequella*, red-necked footman, slender brindle, alder moth, copper underwing and pale pinion have established themselves where they have been previously recorded and are continuing to spread. However, there have been no further records of buff footman.

To the above list must be added the most recent find. On 13th and 14th July 2013, David Bryant caught eight southern wainscot (*Mythimna straminea*) at

Kennet Pans on the estuary of the River Forth. This species is also on the move. It has recently expanded its range in northern England but the only other Scottish records come from the Solway Firth where it was probably first recorded in 1996 and has since been caught at multiple sites along the northern shore of the Firth.

Other moth highlights from the region

David Bryant recorded the first Brussels lace (*Cleorodes lichenaria*) in the region when he caught no less than seven at West Moss-side, near Flanders Moss in June 2012. There is no evidence that this species is moving north; indeed it may have moved south from strongholds in northern Perthshire or, perhaps more likely, is a previously undetected local resident.

The slender-striped rufous (*Coenocalpe lapidata*) is a rare moth of wet flushes in rough upland pasture but, due in part to its late flight time, it is almost certainly under-recorded. It has long seemed likely that it might occur in suitable habitat in our area and on 11th September, Nick Littlewood trapped two and found one other in Glen Finglas.

The barred carpet (*Perizoma taeniata*), a rare moth of shaded woodland has previously featured in this report (Knowler, 2011a) when it was discovered above a damp wooded gully in Lennoxtown. The capture by the author of further examples in the machinery pound at the Visitor Centre of Mugdock Country Park on the 23rd July and 10th of August, 2013 was a considerable surprise but there was suitable habitat nearby.

The chinese character (*Cilix glaucata*) caught by Martin Culshaw in Killearn was the first record for Stirlingshire. Indeed the only other record in the area was nearby in Garlea, Dunbartonshire in 1984. The species is uncommon but widely recorded in southern Scotland and it creeps up the Ayrshire coast but it appears to be on the very edge of its range in west central Scotland (Hill *et al.*, 2010)

A butterbur (*Hydraecia petasitis*) caught in Bridge of Allan by Heather Young in September of 2013 adds to records from Mark Cubitt at Linlithgow Bridge in 2010 and from Martin Culshaw in Killearn in 2011. Thus, there are now recent records of this highly localised moth from across the lowlands of the region and trapping in areas of its foodplant might show that the moth is more common than the few records suggest.

David Bryant's garden at Bridge of Allan has proved particularly productive through 2013. The angle-striped sallow (*Enargia paleacea*) that he caught on 1st Sept was only the third record from the region and the first since 1969. An Angle-barred Pug was the first in the east of the region since 1983 and a Bordered Pug was the first for vice counties 86 and 87 since 1995 although one was caught in vc99 (Dunbartonshire) in 2011.

The publication of a user friendly guide to the micro moths (Sterling *et al.*, 2012) has greatly assisted their identification and records are increasing throughout the region. Both Heather Young and David Bryant recorded the tansy plume (*Gillmeria ochrodactyla*) in their gardens in Bridge of Allan. David Bryant in Bridge of Allan and Martin Culshaw in Killearn both recorded *Orthotella sparganella* and David also recorded Water Veneer (*Acentria ephemerella*) and *Scrobipalpa costella*. All of these were new species for Stirlingshire as was *Argyresthia trifasciata* found in Stirling by two visiting experts on micro-moths.

Favourable weather systems in late summer and particularly early October of 2013 saw the arrival of scarce migrant moths from southern Europe and North Africa into the UK. When this happens most moths are found on the south coast of England and only small numbers make it as far north as central Scotland. A hummingbird hawkmoth (*Macroglossum stellatarum*) was seen in Dumbarton and vestals (*Rhodometra sacraria*) were reported from several parts of Scotland but the only scarce migrant reported in Stirlingshire was the elegant pyralid species, *Palpita vitrealis* caught by David Bryant in Bridge of Allan on October 23rd (Plate 1b). Marilyn Scott also bred another scarce migrant, the scarce bordered straw (*Helicoverpa armigera*) but this individual did not arrive under its own steam. Its passage was assisted as a caterpillar in imported chrysanthemums.

How widespread is the great brocade as a breeding species in our region?

The great brocade (*Eurois occulta*) occurs in the UK in two forms. The typical grey form occurs as a scarce immigrant from Scandinavia, the Netherlands and northern Germany and the most recent definite record of this form in the region was in Mugdock Country Park in 2006; a notable year for migrant moths. There is however a second, essentially black, and to the author's eye, magnificent form of this moth (form *passetii*) which is resident in the western and central highlands of Scotland where it feeds on bog myrtle (*Myrica gale*). The author proved that this form of the species was breeding in Flanders Moss (Knowler, 2012) however the black form has also been recorded from Glen Dubh, Glen Finglass and, in 2011 and three times in 2013, from a Rothamsted trap at Rowardennan on Loch Lomondside. The oak woods at Rowardennan are not the habitat of the moth or of its food plant but the multiple records imply that there is a breeding population not very far away.

Moth species that feed on currants

Two thirds of common and widespread larger moth species have declined in the last 40 years. 37 % of the 337 species for which statistically valid data are available have decreased by at least 50 % (*Fox et al*, 2013). Of these, some of the most dramatic declines have been in those species the larvae of which feed on currants (*Ribes sp*). The most dramatic loss has been the V-moth (*Macaria wauaria*) which has declined by 99 % and the last records from our region were in Milngavie in 1986 and north Bantaskine near Falkirk in 1995. Other currant-feeding species including the spinach moth (*Eulithis mellinata*), phoenix (*Eulithis prunata*) and magpie moth (*Abraxas grossulariata*) have also become much less common and it appears likely that this is because fewer currants are grown both commercially and in gardens and those that are grown may well have been treated with insecticides. The author is keen to identify allotments and gardens with a long history of continuous currant cultivation with minimal use of insecticides where moth trapping might reveal residual populations of these species.

The proposed atlas of moth distribution

Butterfly Conservation, a charity devoted to the conservation of butterflies and moths, has announced its intention to publish an atlas of the distribution of the UK's larger moths in 2018. In a proposed programme of recording in the years leading up to publication it has asked county moth recorders to identify and target 10 km squares that are under-recorded. There are many such squares in our region (Figure 1) and the author will be anxiously seeking volunteers prepared to record in poorly covered regions. Alternatively, those who perhaps have property in poorly recorded 10 km squares but do not want to record moths themselves might be prepared to allow trapping on their properties.

Moth records should be sent to John T. Knowler, the moth recorder for vice counties 86 and 87 (and 99). He will be very happy to assist those who would like to start moth recording and to help anyone with moth identification; particularly if reasonable quality photographs are sent to john.knowler@ntlworld.com

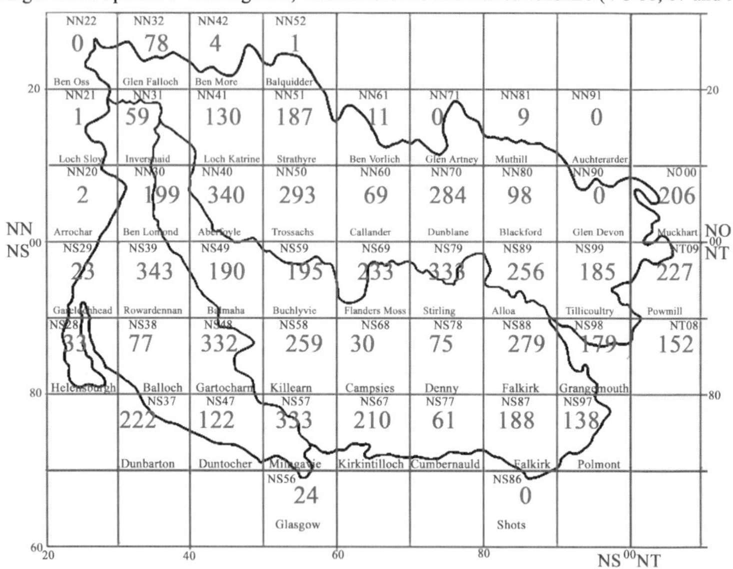

Figure 1. The number of larger moth species recorded in each 10 km square within Stirlingshire, West Perthshire and Dunbartonshire. Notations in each square are of the grid reference of the square, the most obvious topographical feature in the square as well as the number of larger moth species recorded. Portions of 10 km squares in other vice counties are not included in the species count.

Acknowledgements

Thanks to all the moth recorders who have sent their data to the author and to Penny Knowler for producing Figure 1.

References

Fox, R., *et al* (2013) *The State of Britain's Larger Moths 2013*, Butterfly Conservation and Rothamsted Research, Wareham, Dorset, UK.

Heath, J. and Maitland Emmet, A., 1983, *The Moths and Butterflies of Great Britain and Ireland*, Vol 10, Colchester, Essex: Harley Books.

Hill, L., Randle, Z. Fox, R. and Parsons M. 2010, *Provisional Atlas of the UK's Larger Moths*, Wareham, Dorset: Butterfly Conservation

Knowler, J.T., 2005, *The Glasgow Naturalist*, **24**, 64.

Knowler, J.T. (2010) *Annotated Checklist of the Larger Moths of Stirlingshire, West Perthshire and Dunbartonshire* Glasgow Natural History Society.

Knowler, J.T. 2011a, The Forth Naturalist and Historian **34**, 23-28.

Knowler, J.T., 2011b, *Entomologists Record and Journal of Variation* **123**, 220-221.

Knowler, J.T., 2012, *The Glasgow Naturalist*, 25, 59-69.

Knowler, J.T. and Mitchell, J., 2004, *The Glasgow Naturalist*, **24**, 142-143.

Leverton, R. and Palmer, S., 2009, *Entomologists Record and Journal of Variation* **121**, 129-133.

Sterling, P., Parsons, M. and Lewington, R., 2012, *Field Guide to the Micro Moths of Great Britain and Ireland*, British Wildlife Publishing.

FORTH AREA BIRD REPORT 2013

C. J. Pendlebury

This is the 39th bird report for the *Upper Forth Area*. The area covered by the report comprises the council areas of Falkirk, Clackmannanshire and Stirling but excludes parts of the Clyde drainage basin *such as* Loch Lomondside and the Endrick Water area (including Fintry and Balfron), all of which are covered by the Clyde bird report. The report consists of a summary of the main bird news from 2013, followed by detailed species accounts, and a Ringing Report written by Ben Darvill.

Chris Pendlebury, the current SOC recorder, can be contacted by e-mail at chris@upperforthbirds.co.uk, by leaving a message on 07798711134, or by mail to 3 Sinclair Street, Dunblane FK15 0AH. Records can be provided by an Excel spreadsheet that can be sourced from Chris, or through the BTO BirdTrack system.

In this report a coded summary of general distribution is included after the species name. The codes used in this report are:

B	Breeding status: widespread (present in more than five 10 km squares)
b	Breeding status: local, scarce (present in fewer than five 10 km squares)
W	Winter status: widespread or often in groups of more than ten
w	Winter status: local, scarce or usually fewer than ten in a group
P or p	Passage (used for species usually absent in winter); P and p used for widespread and local/scarce, respectively, as in winter status above
S or s	Summer visitor (used for species present in summer but which do not normally breed); S and s used for widespread and local/scarce, respectively, as in winter status above.

Rarer species for which a full list of records are provided are highlighted with the use of an asterix (*). Records of rare species are subject to acceptance by the BBRC, SBRC or the local rarities panel. The latter currently consists of Graeme Garner, Cliff Henty, Mark Lewis, Duncan Orr-Ewing, Chris Pendlebury and Andre Thiel. A list of local rarities is available from Chris Pendlebury.

HIGHLIGHTS OF THE YEAR

January

The returning adult ring-billed gull was at Kinneil on the 3rd. A sinensis Cormorant was at Airthrey Loch, BoA on the 4th. Two ruddy duck were at Lake of Menteith on the 9th. A snow bunting flew over Dunblane on the 13th.

February

Two hawfinch recorded at Kippen on the 2nd was the first record for Upper Forth since 1991. 140 snow bunting were at Tyndrum on the 11th.

March

A little auk was off Kinneil on the 10th. A fulmar was off Skinflats on the 24th, along with single shags there and at Kinneil, and a little gull also at Kinneil on the same date. An avocet was at Skinflats on the 30th.

April

The avocet was again at Skinflats on the 1st. A great northern diver was on L Tay off Killin between the 4th and 7th. The avocet was at Kennet Pans on the 12th. A shag was off Blackness on the 13th. Five Taiga bean geese were at Longcarse, Alloa on the 14th. A male marsh harrier flew north over Dunblane on the 23rd.

May

A little ringed plover was at Kinneil on the 1st. Also on the 1st, a singing male snow bunting was at Stob Binnein. Two yellow wagtail were at Skinflats on the 10th. Single common redpolls were recorded at Skinflats and BoA on the 13th. An inland fulmar was recorded on the 21st, with 1 flying west over Falkirk. An adult spoonbill was at Dunrig Moss on the 27th. A female garganey was at Lake of Menteith on the 29th.

June

A hobby was over Kinbuck on the 13th. A very unusual record was an adult long-tailed skua at Earlsburn Resv on the 25th for 20 minutes, before flying off SW.

July

A marsh harrier was at Blackdevon Wetlands on the 12th. A quail was heard at Thornhill on the 22nd and 27th. A common scoter was at Cambus on the 27th.

August

Five sanderling were at Skinflats on the 6th. The ring-billed gull again returned to Kinneil from the 6th, and present till 12th November. A spoonbill was at Kinneil on the 13th. A common crane arrived in the Doune area on the 19th, staying in the vicinity until 5th September. Three little egret were at Alloa Inch on the 19th. The peak number of little egret at Skinflats (3) for the year was recorded on the 22nd, with the spoonbill also present there. Three fulmar were recorded off Kinneil on the 30th.

September

A little stint was at Skinflats on the 7th, with a fulmar off Kinneil on the same day. A black tern was off Kinneil on the 7th and 8th. The peak number of little egret at Kinneil (3) for the year was recorded on the 14th. A hobby was over Torrie, near Callander on the 19th. A great skua was off Blackness on the 20th.

Two brent geese flew past Bo'ness on the 25th. Another great skua was off Kinneil on the 29th. A family party of bearded tit was recorded at a confidential location during the late summer.

October
A shag was off Blackness on the 14th. One brent goose was at Gart GPs, Callander on the 26th. A gannet was on Lake of Menteith on the 28th.

November
A great northern diver was off Bo'ness on the 23rd. A redhead smew arrived at Blairdrummond GPs on the 24th, staying until the end of the year.

December
The Slamannan Plateau Taiga bean geese peaked at 214 on the 1st. A great northern diver was off Kinneil on the 15th. A good count of red-throated diver was made on the 31st, with 16 at Bo'ness and 2 at Kinneil.

CONTRIBUTORS

This report has been compiled from records submitted by the contributors listed below. Where initials are given, the contributors are listed in species entries of birds that are rare, uncommon or otherwise noteworthy. The editors are grateful to all the contributors for submitting their records. Thanks also go to Mike Bell and Neil Bielby who made available WeBS and BBS count data. Apologies to anyone who has been inadvertently missed out.

S. Abbott (SA), D. Anderson (DA), P. Ashworth (PMA), D. Beaumont (DB), J. Bell (JJB), M. Bell (MVB), P. Dickson (PD), N. Bielby (NB), A. Blair (AB), D. Breckenbridge (DBr), R. Broad (RB), P. Brooks (PB), K. Broomfield (KB), D Bryant (DMB), J Callandine (JRC), A. Carrington-Cotton (ACC), E. Champness (EC), R. Critchlow (RCr), R. Dalziel (RD), B. Darvill (BD), K Duffy (KD), L. Du Feu (LDF), R. Elliot (RE), A. Everingham (AE), T. Findlay (TF), G. Garner (GG), T. Goater (TG), R. Gooch (RG), J. Gordon (JG), D. Grant (DG), A. Hamilton (AHa), C. Henty (CJH), J Holland (JPH), L. Lamont (LLa), E. & G. Leisk (GEL), L. Li (LL), N. Littlewood (NL), G. Martin (GMM), P. Mathews (PM), M. McDonald (MMcD), E. McGuire (EMcG), R. McGregor (RMM), C. McInerny (CMcI), A. McIver (AMacL), B Minshull (BCM), M. Moss (MM), A. Muirhead (AMu), J. Nugent (JHN), L. Oldershaw (LEO), D. Orr-Ewing (DOE), B. Paterson (BP), C. Pendlebury (CJP), K Ranson (KR), A. Renwick (AR), C. Renwick (CRe), N. Richardson (NWR), G. Robertson (GR), A. Robinson (ARo), R Shand (RS), I. Spense (IMS), C. Tatchlet (CT), D. Taylor (DTa), B. Thompson (BJT), D Thorogood (DT), K Waite (KW), R. Whytock (RTW), G. Wilkinson (GW), S. Wilkinson (SW).

SYSTEMATIC LIST

Codes - S, F and C refer to Stirling, Falkirk and Clackmannanshire Council Areas.

MUTE SWAN *Cygnus olor* (B, W)

Inland WeBS: 265 in Jan, 250 in Feb, 240 in Mar, 161 in Sep, 221 in Oct, 176 in Nov and 179 in Dec.

Forth Est WeBS: 29 in Jan, 18 in Feb, 10 in Mar, 67 in Sep, 58 in Oct, 32 in Nov and 22 in Dec.

F Breeding: pr and 1 Y Union Canal, Falkirk 22 Sep; pr and 2 Y Callendar Park, Falkirk 15 Nov. Max: 66 Skinflats 22 Sep; 6 Forth/Clyde Canal, Falkirk 24 Jan.

C Max: 34 Gartmorn Dam 16 Mar and 5 Apr; 7 Cambus 18 Aug.

S Breeding: pr ON Airthrey L, BoA 9 Apr; pr Lake of Menteith 25 May; pr and 3 Y Cromlix House L 29 Jun; pr and 6 Y Ochlochy Pond, Dunblane 2 Jul. Max: 22 L Watston, Doune 13 Jan; 17 Craigforth, Stirling 19 Jan; 18 Fallin 29 Mar; 45 Airthrey L, BoA 12 Apr; 20 Lake of Menteith 26 May.

WHOOPER SWAN *Cygnus cygnus* (W)

Spring departure: 1 Skinflats 17 May (PB). Autumn arrival: 2 Craigforth, Stirling 22 Sep (GW).

Inland WeBS: 36 in Jan, 38 in Feb, 32 in Mar, 2 in Sep, 4 in Oct, 22 in Nov and 19 in Dec.

Forth Est WeBS: 2 in Jan, 0 in Feb, 0 in Mar, 0 in Sep, 2 in Oct, 2 in Nov and 0 in Dec.

F Winter/spring max: 12 Skinflats 5 Jan. Autumn/winter max: 9 > Carronshore 28 Oct; 11 Skinflats 13 Oct.

C Winter/spring max: 2 Gartmorn Dam 3 Mar. Autumn/winter max: 7 Gartmorn Dam 11 Dec, 2 Alloa 7 Dec.

S Winter/spring max: 19 L Dochart 19 Jan; 16 L Lubhair 16 Mar. Autumn/winter max: 19 S > Argaty, BoD 25 Oct; 14 Doune 2 Nov; 16 L Dochart 26 Nov.

BEAN GOOSE *Anser fabalis* (W)

F Regular wintering flock of Taiga race birds in the vicinity of the Slamannan Plateau. Autumn/winter: 154 Slamannan 30 Sep, 165 there 13 Oct, 214 there 1 Dec (AMacI).

C Five Taiga race birds Longcarse, Alloa 14 Apr (JRC).

PINK-FOOTED GOOSE *Anser brachyrhynchus* (W)

Spring departure: 1 Skinflats 26 May (PB). Autumn arrival: 100 Skinflats 16 Sep (AE).

Forth Est WeBS: 495 in Jan, 512 in Feb, 881 in Mar, 202 in Sep, 116 in Oct, 0 in Nov and 408 in Dec.

F Winter/spring max: 600 Skinflats 3 Feb. Autumn/winter max: 1500 Gardrum Moss 27 Sep; 4025 Skinflats 16 Dec.

C Winter/spring max: 1000 Tullibody Inch 29 Jan; 1072 Alloa Inch 25 Feb; 3000 Cambus 29 Mar. Autumn/winter max: 1150 Alloa Inch 11 Oct; 1694 Kennet Pans 21 Nov.

S Winter/spring max: 1100 Lecropt Carse 26 Jan; 2000 Kinbuck 6 Feb. Autumn/winter max: 540 Flanders Moss 21 Sep; 750 Thornhill 2 Oct; 1070 Blairdrummond Moss 23 Dec.

GREYLAG GOOSE *Anser anser* (b, W)

Spring departure and autumn arrival are muddied by the presence of resident feral birds.

Forth Est WeBS: 54 in Jan, 38 in Feb, 9 in Mar, 880 in Sep, 37 in Oct, 50 in Nov and 88 in Dec.

F Winter/spring max: 15 Carriden, Bo'ness 2 Feb. Autumn/winter max: 270 Blackness

8 Aug; 31 Skinflats 11 Aug.

C Winter/spring max: 240 Alva 11 Feb. Autumn/winter max: 460 Cambus 31 Aug; 880 Cambus 24 Sep.

S Winter/spring: 217 Ashfield 23 Feb; 300 Blairdrummond GPs 3 May. Autumn/winter: 180 L Watston, Doune 13 Oct; 250 Blairdrummond GPs 8 Nov; 362 L Coulter 23 Nov.

CANADA GOOSE *Branta canadensis* (b W)

Inland WeBS: 515 in Jan, 530 in Feb, 481 in Mar, 1495 in Sep, 542 in Oct, 557 in Nov and 886 in Dec.

F Site max: 1 Kinneil 16 Mar; 2 Carronshore 23 Mar; 64 Skinflats 17 Sep; 85 Gardrum Moss 27 Sep.

C Breeding: 2 pr Gartmorn Dam 20 Mar. Site max: 3 Tullibody Inch 29 Jan; 50 Gartmorn Dam 8 Oct.

S Breeding: 26 ad and 6 Y Gart GP, Callander 5 May. Max: 350 Gart GP, Callander 30 Aug; 634 L Rusky 5 Sep; 147 N Third Resv 7 Sep; 171 L Coulter 23 Nov; 258 Lake of Menteith 17 Dec; 126 Killin marshes 22 Dec.

*BARNACLE GOOSE *Branta leucopsis* (w)

In our area it is difficult to distinguish between wild migrants and feral birds resident in Britain.

F Six Skinflats 17 Nov (MVB).

C Three Cambus 29 Mar (ACC). 2 Alloa Inch 31 Mar (JRC). 1 Alloa Inch 11 Oct (JRC).

S Three Flanders Moss 4 Feb (RTW). 1 Gargunnock 21 Feb (DMB). 1 L Rusky 5 Sep (NB). 7 Ashfield 15 Dec (CJP). 4 Lecropt Carse 15 Dec and 2 Drip Moss, Stirling 30 Dec (DOE).

*BRENT GOOSE *Branta bernicla* (w)

F Two > SE at Bo'ness 25 Sep (GG).

S One Gart GPs, Callander 26 Oct (NB)

COMMON SHELDUCK *Tadorna tadorna* (b, W)

Inland WeBS: 2 in Jan, 1 in Feb, 16 in Mar, 0 in Sep, 0 in Oct, 2 in Nov and 2 in Dec. Forth Est WeBS: 557 in Jan, 679 in Feb, 432 in Mar, 1783 in Sep, 819 in Oct, 458 in Nov and 456 in Dec.

F Moult flock max count of 4109 Grangemouth 2 Aug (DMB).

C Site max: 30 Tullibody Inch 29 Jan; 21 Cambus 29 Mar.

S One F Mid Cambushinnie, Kinbuck 25 Apr.

EURASIAN WIGEON *Anas penelope* (s, W)

Inland WeBS: 200 in Jan, 326 in Feb, 250 in Mar, 20 in Sep, 142 in Oct, 192 in Nov and 327 in Dec.

Forth Est WeBS: 229 in Jan, 162 in Feb, 227 in Mar, 165 in Sep, 280 in Oct, 447 in Nov and 412 in Dec.

F Winter/spring max: 426 S Alloa 1 Feb. Autumn/winter max: 240 Skinflats 7 Sep; 400 Blackness 14 Oct; 195 S Alloa 15 Dec.

C Winter/spring max: 95 Tullibody Inch 29 Jan; 10 Gartmorn Dam 16 Mar. Autumn/winter max: 18 Gartmorn Dam 4 Dec; 41 Cambus 12 Dec.

S Winter/spring max: 43 L Watston, Doune 13 Jan; 58 Killin 9 Feb; 38 Gart GPs, Callander 21 Feb. 48 Kinbuck 23 Feb. Autumn/winter max: 46 L Coulter 23 Nov; 65 Gart GPs, Callander 1 Dec; 200 Lecropt Carse 30 Dec.

*GADWALL *Anas strepera* (s, w)

F Four Kinneil 13 Jan, with 2 still 20th (JRC, CJP). 2 Skinflats 3 Mar (AB). 2 Skinflats 15 Apr (GG). 3 Skinflats 12 Nov, 2 still 17th (NB, MVB).

C Two Cambus 12 and 13 Apr (JRC). 5 Blackdevon Wetlands 14 Apr (DMB). 2 Alloa Inch 14 Apr (JRC). 3 Gartmorn Dam 16 Sept, 10 there 20 Oct (PMA, DMB). 2 Alloa Inch 31 Dec (JRC).

EURASIAN TEAL *Anas crecca* (b, W)

Inland WeBS: 921 in Jan, 908 in Feb, 930 in Mar, 665 in Sep, 1083 in Oct, 1168 in Nov and 1337 in Dec.

Forth Est WeBS: 1034 in Jan, 1346 in Feb, 700 in Mar, 642 in Sep, 637 in Oct, 882 in Nov and 1414 in Dec.

F Winter/spring max: 392 S Alloa 1 Feb; 764 Kinneil and 301 Skinflats 10 Feb. Summer: 2 Dunrig Moss 16 Jul. Autumn/winter max: 393 Skinflats 15 Dec.

C Winter/spring max: 206 Cambus 4 Jan; 435 Tullibody Inch 29 Jan and 340 Kennet Pans 30th. Autumn/winter max: 122 Cambus 22 Sep; 325 Alloa Inch and 107 Kennet Pans 15 Dec.

S Winter/spring max: 50 Cambushinnie, Kinbuck 23 Feb. Autumn/winter max: 85 L Dochart 13 Oct; 81 N Third Resv 20 Oct; 52 L Coulter 23 Nov; 163 Gart GPs, Callander 1 Dec; 120 Lecropt Carse 30 Dec.

MALLARD *Anas platyrhynchos* (B, W)

Inland WeBS: 1880 in Jan, 2273 in Feb, 1563 in Mar, 1988 in Sep, 2267 in Oct, 2099 in Nov and 2220 in Dec.

Forth Est WeBS: 314 in Jan, 181 in Feb, 148 in Mar, 371 in Sep, 204 in Oct, 312 in Nov and 306 in Dec.

F Max: 220 Skinflats 16 Aug; 230 S Alloa 22 Sep; 50 Bo'ness 9 Nov; 31 Callendar Park, Falkirk 15 Nov.

C Max: 100 Tullibody Inch 29 Jan; 80 Gartmorn Dam Sep-Nov; 26 Cambus 13 Oct.

S Max: 142 Lake of Menteith 8 Feb; 100 Callander 26 Mar; 130 L Watston, Doune 15 Sep; 99 Doune ponds 4 Nov; 159 Airthrey L, BoA 29 Nov; 112 Gart GPs, Callander 1 Dec; 97 Blairdrummond GPs 14 Dec; 182 Killin marshes 22 Dec; 90 Lecropt Carse 30 Dec.

NORTHERN PINTAIL *Anas acuta* (W)

Forth Est WeBS: 28 in Jan, 62 in Feb, 65 in Mar, 1 in Sep, 9 in Oct, 48 in Nov and 64 in Dec.

F Winter/spring max: 65 Skinflats 10 Mar and 16 Kinneil 2 Mar. Autumn/winter max: 56 Skinflats 15 Dec.

C One M Gartmorn Dam 28 Feb (RE), and 3 F there 20 Oct (DMB).

*GARGANEY *Anas querquedula* (s)

S One F Lake of Menteith 29 May (RTW). This is the 22nd record of this species in our recording area.

*NORTHERN SHOVELER *Anas clypeata* (p)

F One F Kinneil 26 May (RS). 4 Skinflats 11 Aug to 7 Oct (AB, GG, RTW, DOE).

C One Longcarse, Alloa 14 Apr (JRC).

COMMON POCHARD *Aythya ferina* (W)

Inland WeBS: 7 in Jan, 9 in Feb, 8 in Mar, 1 in Sep, 7 in Oct, 19 in Nov and 13 in Dec.

F Nine Skinflats 21 to 23 Mar, with singles until 19 Jun (GG, DOE, AB et al.).

C Two Gartmorn Dam 16 Mar (PMA).

S Six Killin, L Tay 23 Feb, and 1 on 23 to 30 Nov (JPH). Lake of Menteith: 1 on 8 to 16 Mar, and autumn/winter peak of 14 on 10 Oct (RTW). Gart GPs, Callander: singles on 26 Mar, 5 May, 16 Jun and 6 Oct (NB). 1 Daldorn, Doune 14 Apr (DOE). 1 Blairdrummond GPs 25 Aug to 21 Sep, and 2 on 5 Oct (DOE).

TUFTED DUCK *Aythya fuligula* (B, W)

Inland WeBS: 229 in Jan, 339 in Feb, 346 in Mar, 175 in Sep, 417 in Oct, 346 in Nov and 352 in Dec.

F Winter/spring max: 12 Falkirk 24 Jan; 20 Larbert House 24 Mar. Summer: 8 Skinflats 12 May to 19 Jun; F and br/4 Darnrig Moss 16 Jul. Autumn/winter max: 8 Larbert House 9 Oct; 12 Skinflats 3 Nov.

C Winter/spring max: 60 Gartmorn Dam 5 Apr. Breeding: F and br/5 Blackdevon Wetlands 12 Aug. Autumn/winter max: 60 Gartmorn Dam 8 Oct and 10 Nov.

S Winter/spring max: 47 Blairdrummond 27 Mar. Breeding: F and br/6 Ochlochy Pond, Dunblane 20 Jul. Autumn/winter max: 75 Gart GPs, Callander 4 Aug; 40 Blairdrummond GPs, 27 Oct; 88 Lake of Menteith 17 Dec.

GREATER SCAUP *Aythya marina* (s, w)

Forth Est WeBS: 19 in Jan, 8 in Feb, 19 in Mar, 0 in Sep, 5 in Oct, 6 in Nov and 0 in Dec.

F Skinflats: 1 on 7 Jan, 1 on 9 to 11 Aug, 2 on 7 Sep, 1 on 16 to 17 Sep, 1 on 20 Oct, and 1 on 3 Nov. Kinneil max: 19 in Jan, 13 in Feb, 23 in Mar, 4 in Apr and May, 2 in Jul and Aug, 11 in Sep, 1 in Nov. 17 Blackness 8 and 16 Feb. 24 Bo'ness 23 to 30 Mar.

COMMON EIDER *Somateria mollissima* (s, w)

Forth Est WeBS: 6 in Jan, 6 in Feb, 23 in Mar, 7 in Sep, 5 in Oct, 2 in Nov and 0 in Dec.

F Skinflats max: 4 in Jan, 3 in Feb, 21 in Mar, 10 in Oct, and 4 in Nov. Kinneil max: 3 in Mar, 2 in May, 8 in Aug, 11 in Sep, and 2 in Nov. Bo'ness: max of 16 on 2 Feb. Blackness: max of 42 on 20 Sep.

C Two Kennet Pans 12 Apr.

*LONG-TAILED DUCK *Clangula hyemalis* (w)

F One Skinflats 13 Jan (MVB). 3 Bo'ness 20 Jan and 2 Feb, and 1 there 23 Mar (GG, DMB). 1 Kinneil 10 Mar (JRC).

C One R Devon, Cambus 2 Jan (JRC). 2 F/imm Gartmorn Dam 20 and 31 Oct (DMB, RE).

S One Lake of Menteith 28 Oct and 18 Nov (RTW). 1 N Third Resv 13 Nov (LEO). 1 Blairdrummond GPs 17 Nov (DOE).

*COMMON SCOTER *Melanitta nigra* (w)

Forth Est WeBS: 14 in Jan, 26 in Feb, 19 in Mar, 0 in Sep, 0 in Oct, 0 in Nov and 0 in Dec.

F Bo'ness max: 25 in Jan, 26 in Feb; 7 in Mar (DMB, JRC, GG). Kinneil: 19 on 10 Mar, 2 on 26 Sep, 25 on 12 Nov (JRC, DT).

C One Cambus 27 Jul (DMB).

COMMON GOLDENEYE *Bucephala clangula* (W)

Inland WeBS: 292 in Jan, 375 in Feb, 427 in Mar, 0 in Sep, 38 in Oct, 213 in Nov and 333 in Dec.

Forth Est WeBS: 38 in Jan, 26 in Feb, 13 in Mar, 0 in Sep, 0 in Oct, 11 in Nov and 38 in Dec.

F Max: 20 Skinflats 10 Jan; 17 S Alloa 1 Feb; 24 Dunmore 12 Feb; 10 Carronshore 23 Mar; 15 Skinflats 31 Mar.

C Max: 49 Tullibody Inch 29 Jan; 22 Cambus 18 Feb; 26 Gartmorn Dam 5 Apr.

S Max: 25 Killin, L Tay 9 Feb; 168 Lake of Menteith 17 Dec; 34 Lecropt Carse 30 Dec.

*SMEW *Mergellus albellus* (w)

S One redhead Blairdrummond GPs 24 Nov to year-end (DOE, PB, DMB).

RED-BREASTED MERGANSER *Mergus serrator* (B, W)

Inland WeBS: 12 in Jan, 9 in Feb, 18 in Mar, 2 in Sep, 4 in Oct, 15 in Nov and 3 in Dec.

Forth Est WeBS: 66 in Jan, 22 in Feb, 26 in Mar, 16 in Sep, 33 in Oct, 80 in Nov and 44 in Dec.

F Max: 40 Kinneil 5 Aug; 18 Bo'ness 8 Sep; 23 Skinflats 17 Nov.

C One Cambus 18 Feb.

S Lecropt Carse max: 5 on 26 Jan. Singles at Killin, Loch Tay on 5-6 Apr and 1 Jun.

GOOSANDER *Mergus merganser* (B, W)

Inland WeBS: 88 in Jan, 124 in Feb, 129 in Mar, 65 in Sep, 67 in Oct, 80 in Nov and 128 in Dec.

Forth Est WeBS: 0 in Jan; 1 in Feb, 0 in Mar, 9 in Sep, 25 in Oct, 8 in Nov and 5 in Dec.

F Max: 7 Skinflats 3 Mar; 9 Carronshore 20 Sep; 13 Grangemouth 20 Oct.

C Max: 6 Cambus 13 Oct; 12 Gartmorn Dam 4 Dec.
S Max: 9 Lecropt Carse 19 Feb; 7 Killin, L Tay 14 Mar; 18 Blairdrummond GPs 5 Dec.

*RUDDY DUCK *Oxyura jamaicensis* (w)
S 2 Lake of Menteith 9 Jan, with 1 still 12th (NB, RTW).

*RED GROUSE *Lagopus lagopus* (B, W)
S Two Sgiath Chull 1 Apr (BJT). 2 Dumyat 6 Apr (BD). 2 Sgiath Bhuidhe 15 Jun (JPH).

*ROCK PTARMIGAN *Lagopus muta* (b, w)
S One Ben More 6 Apr (JG). Singles Stob Binnein 1 May and 5 Jun (JRC). 2 Beinn Dubhcraig and 1 Ben Lui 16 Jun (RCr).

BLACK GROUSE *Tetrao tetrix* (b, w)
S Records from: Callander, L Tay, Tyndrum, G Lochay, Gleann Meann (JPH, DOE, NW, GMM, IMS).

RED-LEGGED PARTRIDGE *Alectoris rufa* (b, w)
S Cromlix, BoD: 2 on 29 Mar, and singles on 27 Apr and 23 Jun (DOE). 3 Bracklinn, Callander 19 Jun (DOE).

GREY PARTRIDGE *Perdix perdix* (b, w)
F Six Higgin's Neuk, Airth 17 Sep (ACC). 2 Kinneil 6 Jul (RS). Skinflats max: 2 in May (GG, ACC, AE).
C One Alva 8 Jun (PMA).

*COMMON QUAIL *Coturnix coturnix* (b)
S One Thornhill on 22 and 27 Jul (ARo, RTW).

COMMON PHEASANT *Phasianus colchicus* (B, W)
Large numbers released on shooting estates, otherwise widespread but in smaller numbers.
S Max: 35 Lanrick, Doune 20 Oct.

RED-THROATED DIVER *Gavia stellata* (b, w)
F One Grangepans 22 Jan (DMB). Kinneil: singles on 24 Jan, 15 Feb, and 31 Mar, with 3 on 29 Sep and 2 on 15 Dec (CJP, JRC, DT). On 31 Dec, 16 at Bo'ness and 2 at Kinneil (CJP).
C One Longcarse, Alloa 21 Feb (JRC).
S One at Lake of Menteith 2 to 15 Apr (RTW).

*BLACK-THROATED DIVER *Gavia arctica* (b)
S Two Killin, L Tay 14 Mar and 3 Apr (JPH). Pairs at 3 undisclosed locations in Trossachs in Apr to Jul (SA, RE, RTW, NW).

*GREAT NORTHERN DIVER *Gavia immer* (w)
F 1 Bo'ness 23 Nov (CJP). 1 Kinneil 15 Dec (JRC).
S 1 Killin, L Tay 4 Apr to 7 Apr (JPH).

LITTLE GREBE *Tachybaptus ruficollis* (B, w)
Inland WeBS: 32 in Jan, 47 in Feb, 26 Mar, 92 in Sep, 83 in Oct, 73 in Nov and 37 in Dec.
F Breeding: 4 Y Skinflats 9 Sep. Skinflats max: 14 on 8 Sep. Also 1 at Kinneil curling pond on 20 Apr.
S Breeding: 1 ad ON and 2 Y Cromlix, BoD 29 Jun. Max: 31 Gart GPs, Callander 18 Aug; 11 Blairdrummond GPs 2 Sep.

GREAT CRESTED GREBE *Podiceps cristatus* (b, W)
Inland WeBS: 9 in Jan, 9 in Feb, 36 in Mar, 43 in Sep, 16 in Oct, 11 in Nov and 18 in Dec.
Forth Est WeBS: 3 in Jan, 11 in Feb, 0 in Mar, 12 in Sep, 1 in Oct, 9 in Nov and 0 in Dec.
F Max: 30 Kinneil 17 Sep and 15 Blackness 20 Sep.
C Max: 3 Gartmorn Dam 7 Jul and 10 Nov.
S Max: 15 Gart GPs, Callander 16 Jun; 34 Lake of Menteith 5 Sep.

*NORTHERN FULMAR *Fulmaris glacialis* (s, p)
F One Skinflats 24 Mar (GG). 1 W < Falkirk 21 May (CJP, RMM). 3 Kinneil 30 Aug (DT). 1 Bo'ness 7 Sep (GG).

NORTHERN GANNET *Morus bassanus* (p)

F 16 Kinneil 29 Sep (CJP). Singles Blackness and Skinflats 1 Oct (DOE, PB). Skinflats in Oct: 1 on 5th, 3 on 7th, 3 on 8th (AE, GG, DMB). Singles at Kinneil 29 Oct and 12 Nov (DT).

S 1 Lake of Menteith 28 Oct (RTW).

GREAT CORMORANT *Phalacrocorax carbo* (S, W)

Inland WeBS: 66 in Jan, 89 in Feb, 89 in Mar, 40 in Sep, 91 in Oct, 93 in Nov and 60 in Dec.

Forth Est WeBS: 57 in Jan, 37 in Feb, 40 in Mar, 49 in Sep, 60 in Oct, 83 in Nov and 51 in Dec.

F Max: 25 Bo'ness 2 Feb; 28 Skinflats 28 Oct.

C Max: 15 Gartmorn Dam 10 Nov; 35 Alloa Inch 17 Nov.

S Max: 22 Lake of Menteith 8 Feb; 6 Carron Valley Resv 31 May; 25 Killin, L Tay 21 Nov.

One sinensis race bird at Airthrey L, BoA 4 Jan (ACC), pending acceptance by SBRC; likely to be the bird recorded in Jan 2014 and accepted by SBRC, which is the only record for the region.

*SHAG *Phalacrocorax aristotelis* (p)

F Singles Kinneil (CJP) and Skinflats (GG) 24 Mar. Singles Blackness 13 Apr (LDF) and 14 Oct (DMB).

*LITTLE EGRET *Egretta garzetta* (w)

F One Skinflats 2 Jan (AB), present from 15 Dec. Singles at Skinflats, Kinneil and Airth between 12 Aug and 22 Dec, with 3 at Skinflats 22 Aug and Kinneil 14 Sep (GG, RTW, CJP et al.); this is the 14th record for the recording area.

C One Kennet Pans 25 Aug (JRC). 3 Alloa Inch 19 Sep (DMB).

GREY HERON *Ardea cinerea* (B,W)

Inland WeBS: 53 in Jan, 68 in Feb, 43 in Mar, 89 in Sep, 87 in Oct, 73 in Nov and 68 in Dec.

Forth Est WeBS: 37 in Jan, 9 in Feb, 3 in Mar, 48 in Sep, 23 in Oct, 30 in Nov and 27 in Dec.

F Breeding: 19 AONs Dunmore, 33 discarded eggs (AB). Max: 4 Kinneil 12 Jan; 23 Skinflats 22 Sep.

C Max: 5 Tullibody Inch 29 Jan; 4 Gartmorn Dam 16 Mar; 8 Cambus 22 Sep.

S Max: 10 Lecropt Carse 26 Jan; 14 Gart GPs, Callander 4 Aug; 9 Blairdrummond GPs 5 Oct.

SPOONBILL *Platalea leucorodia* (s)

F Ad Dunrig Moss, Slamannan Plateau 27 May (TF). Single Kinneil 13 Aug (DT) and Skinflats 22nd (TF, GG).

HONEY BUZZARD *Pernis apivorus* (b?)

S Male at undisclosed location in Trossachs on 21 May, 28 Aug and 3 Sep (CMcI *et al.*)

RED KITE *Milvus milvus* (b ,W)

C One The Law, Alva 3 Sep (KB).

S Breeding: of 33 prs 27 laid eggs, 17 prs successfully fledging 31 Y (DOE, MMcD, DA). Argaty, BoD max: 48 on 27 Jan (DOE). Regular in areas of BoD, Stirling, and Callander. Also recorded at Tyndrum.

*WHITE-TAILED EAGLE *Haliaeetus albicilla* (s, w)

All likely to refer to birds from the Fife reintroduction scheme.

C One > Menstrie Glen 24 Jan (JRC).

S One > Hill of Row, Dunblane and Mill of Argaty, BoD 27 Jan (KD, DOE). 1 > BoA 19 Mar (RMM, CJP). 1 Tyndrum 13 Jul and Crianlarich 2 Aug (JPH, JJB). 1 > Blackdub, Stirling 14 Dec (MVB).

MARSH HARRIER *Circus aeruginosus* (p, s)

C One Blackdeven Wetlands 12 Jul (JRC).

S One M > Dunblane 23 Apr (CJP).

HEN HARRIER *Circus cyaneus* (b, w)

S One M Cromlix 5 and 15 Jan (DOE, KD). One Tyndrum 21 Mar (JPH). M and F Waterside, BoD 20 Sep (KD). 1 L Watston, Doune 15 Dec (DOE).

*NORTHERN GOSHAWK *Accipiter gentilis* (b, w)

S Breeding: 3 pairs fledgling 2, 3 and 3 Y (DA). Also 1 Blairdrummond GPs 14 Sep (DOE).

EURASIAN SPARROWHAWK *Accipiter nisus* (B, W)

Recorded throughout the majority of the recording area. Contributors are encouraged to submit breeding records.

COMMON BUZZARD *Buteo buteo* (B, W)

Inland WeBS counts: 42 in Jan, 40 in Feb, 32 in Mar, 43 in Sep, 47 in Oct, 58 in Nov and 44 in Dec.

Recorded throughout the majority of the recording area; breeding data were unfortunately unavailable for 2013.

GOLDEN EAGLE *Aquila chrysaetos* (s, w)

S One Crianlarich 2 Aug (JJB).

OSPREY *Pandion haliaetus* (B)

First record of the year: 1 Polmont 15 Mar (DOE)

F Also 1 Kinneil 6 Apr (EMcG, CJP).

C One Gartmorn Dam 4 May (JRC).

S Breeding: of 26 pairs present, 18-22 laid clutches, raising 30 Y (DA, RB, DOE). Summer: present throughout region, particularly Callander, Doune, Lake of Menteith, L Achray, N Third Resv and L Coulter.

COMMON KESTREL *Falco tinnunculus* (B, W)

Recorded throughout most of the recording area. Contributors are encouraged to submit breeding records.

MERLIN *Falco columbarius* (b?, w)

F F Skinflats 6 Jan (GG). M Darnrig Moss 24 Oct (BCM). F Airth 21 Nov (DMB). F Skinflats 7 Dec (DMB).

S One Ashfield 1 Jan (CJP). 1 Tyndrum 21 Mar (JPH). F Blairdrummond GPs 11 Dec (DMB). 1 Lecropt Carse 30 Dec (DOE).

HOBBY *Falco subbuteo*

S One Kinbuck 13 Jun (KD). 1 Torrie, Callander 19 Sep (DA).

PEREGRINE FALCON *Falco peregrinus* (B, W)

F Up to two individuals throughout year Kinneil, Skinflats and Airth areas.

C Singles Alva 22 Apr and Tillicoultry 26 Aug.

S One Dunblane and Lecropt Carse in Jan. Summer: up to two individuals at BoD, Lake of Menteith, Sgaith a'Chaise and Tyndrum. Autumn/winter: singles at Callander, Aberfoyle, Stronachlachar and G Finglas.

WATER RAIL *Rallus aquaticus* (b, w)

F Skinflats: throughout year, max 2 (GG, RS *et al.*). 2 Kinneil 20 Apr (CJP).

C Max: 4 Cambus 9 Jul, 2 Blackdevon Wetlands 28 Sep, 3 Tullibody Inch 22 Nov, 4 Alloa Inch 31 Dec (JRC, DMB).

S 1 Killin, L Tay 2 Jun (JPH). 2 L Watston, Doune 5 Sep (DMB).

COMMON MOORHEN *Gallinula chloropus* (B,W)

Inland WeBS: 43 in Jan, 45 in Feb, 45 in Mar, 66 in Sep, 70 in Oct, 92 in Nov and 77 in Dec.

F Max: 7 Callendar Park, Falkirk 8 Jan; 6 Mungal ponds, Falkirk 17 Feb; 10 Skinflats 24 Aug.

C Max: 4 Cambus 26 Oct.
S Max: 21 Airthrey L, BoA 29 Nov.

COMMON COOT *Fulica atra* (B, W)
Inland WeBS: 109 in Jan, 147 in Feb, 114 in Mar, 44 in Sep, 115 in Oct, 75 in Nov and 120 in Dec.
F Max: 17 Larbert Ho 15 Jul; 28 Skinflats 1 Sep.
C Max: 7 Gartmorn Dam 23 Mar.
S Max: 29 L Watston, Doune 13 Jan; 43 Lake of Menteith 27 Nov; 66 Airthrey L, BoA 29 Nov.

*COMMON CRANE *Grus grus*
S One adult in Doune / Callander area: Broich Fm on 19 Aug, Gart GPs on 30 Aug, and by L Watston on 2 and 5 Sep (PD, NB, PB, SW, DMB). This is the third record for the region.

EURASIAN OYSTERCATCHER *Haematopus ostralegus* (B, W)
Forth Est WeBS: 398 in Jan, 412 in Feb, 245 in Mar, 184 in Sep, 85 in Oct, 219 in Nov and 245 in Dec.
Inland WeBS: 0 in Jan, 145 in Feb, 403 in Mar, 1 in Sep, 0 in Oct, 1 in Nov and 2 in Dec.
F Max: 140 Skinflats 24 Aug; 380 Kinneil 28 Nov; 36 Blackness 11 Dec.
C Max: 12 Alva 24 Feb.
S Max: 137 Blairdrummond 3 Mar; 51 Kinbuck 24 Mar.

*AVOCET *Recurvirostra avosetta*
F One Skinflats 30 Mar to 1 Apr (RS, GG *et al.*)
C One Kennet Pans 12 Apr (JRC).

*LITTLE RINGED PLOVER *Charadrius dubius*
S One Kinneil 1 May (DMB). This is the 21st record for the area since modern recording began in 1974.

COMMON RINGED PLOVER *Charadrius hiaticula* (b, W)
Forth Est WeBS: 0 in Jan, 0 in Feb, 5 in Mar, 29 in Sep, 5 in Oct, 7 in Nov and 0 in Dec.
F Max: 40 Blackness 5 Aug; 35 Skinflats 19 Aug; 25 Kinneil 31 Aug.
C Breeding: pr and juv Forestmill 10 Jul; ad and juv Kennet Pans 23 Jul. Max: 34 Kennet Pans 26 Apr.
S Summer: 2 pr Kildean, Stirling 26 Apr. Max: 4 Gart GPs, Callander 26 Mar.

EUROPEAN GOLDEN PLOVER *Pluvialis apricaria* (B, W)
Forth Est WeBS: 16 in Jan, 0 in Feb, 0 in Mar, 68 in Sep, 437 in Oct, 40 in Nov and 0 in Dec.
F Winter/spring max: 1000 Kinneil 12 Jan. Autumn/winter max: 13 Blackness 20 Sep; 65 Skinflats 22 Sep; 450 Kinneil 18 Oct.
C One Craig Leith, Alva 17 Feb.
S One over Ashfield 1 Jan. Summer: 8 Kirkton, Tyndrum 12 Apr; 1 Stuc a' Chroin 18 Jul.

GREY PLOVER *Pluvialis squatarola* (W)
F In Jan singles Kinneil on 12th and Kincardine Br on 13th, and 7 Skinflats on 20th. Singles Kinneil 6 Apr, Skinflats 17 Jun and Kinneil 4 Aug. Oct max: 6 Skinflats 8th, 1 Blackness 14th, 6 Kinneil 26th. 8 Skinflats 3 Nov. 3 Kincardine Br 17 Nov.

NORTHERN LAPWING *Vanellus vanellus* (B, W)
Forth Est WeBS: 24 in Jan, 372 in Feb, 5 in Mar, 611 in Sep, 774 in Oct, 610 in Nov and 238 in Dec.
Inland WeBS: 464 in Jan, 75 in Feb, 132 in Mar, 826 in Sep, 74 in Oct, 203 in Nov and 41 in Dec.
F Breeding: 16 on territory Kinneil 1 May. Max: 187 Darnrig Moss 10 Sep; 204 Skinflats 22 Nov; 656 Kinneil 20 Oct.

C Winter/spring max: 70 Tullibody Inch 29 Jan; 185 Cambus 18 Feb. Autumn/winter max: 304 R Forth, Alloa 24 Sep.

S Winter/spring max: 130 Kinbuck 6 Feb; 115 Lecropt Carse 19 Feb; 84 Blairdrummond GPs 3 Mar. Autumn/winter max: 90 Gart GPs, Callander 4 Aug; 57 Blairdrummond GPs 25 Aug; 111 L Coulter 23 Nov.

RED KNOT *Calidris canutus* (W)

Forth Est WeBS: 4654 in Jan, 2975 in Feb, 490 in Mar, 26 in Sep, 0 in Oct, 52 in Nov and 31 in Dec.

F Winter/spring max: 4652 Kinneil and 1030 Skinflats 13 Jan. Autumn/winter max: 85 Kinneil 1 Oct; 100 Bo'ness 9 Nov.

SANDERLING *Calidris alba*

F Five Kinneil 6 Aug (DT).

*LITTLE STINT *Calidris minuta*

F One Skinflats 7 Sep (DOE, GG).

CURLEW SANDPIPER *Calidris ferruginea* (p)

F One juv Skinflats 7-9 Sep (GG, PB, DMB). Singles Kinneil 8 and 17 Sep (RS). 1 Skinflats 22 Sep (MVB). 2 Kinneil 29 Sep (CJP). 1 Skinflats 8 Oct (DMB).

C Two Longcarse, Alloa 25 Sep (JRC).

DUNLIN *Calidris alpina* (b?, W)

Forth Est WeBS: 2249 in Jan, 4550 in Feb, 1387 in Mar, 366 in Sep, 1148 in Oct, 1295 in Nov and 1729 in Dec.

F Winter/spring max: 4000 Kinneil 21 Jan; 170 S Alloa 1 Feb; 1040 Skinflats 10 Feb. Autumn/winter max: 67 Blackness 14 Oct; 1000 Skinflats 3 Nov; 1500 Kinneil 29 Dec.

C Longcarse, Alloa: Aug peak of 31 on 31st (JRC).

S Summer: 1 male on territory at BoD 1 Jun (KD).

RUFF *Philomachus pugnax* (w, p)

F Skinflats: first of autumn on 13 Aug (RTW); Aug max of 6 on 24th (DOE); Sep max of 8 on 9th (DMB). 1 Airth 6 Sep (DMB). Kinneil: singles 16 Sep to 1 Oct (DOE, RS, ACC, DMB), with 2 there 26 Oct (GR); 1 on 29 Dec (AB) presumably over-wintering.

JACK SNIPE *Lymnocryptes minimus* (w)

Inland WeBS: 1 in Jan, 0 in Feb, 3 in Mar, 0 in Sep, 2 in Oct, 2 in Nov and 2 in Dec.

F Two Kinneil 20 and 27 Jan (CJP).

C One Kennet pans 12 Feb (DMB). 1 Menstrie Moss 17 Feb (MM). 1 Longcarse, Alloa 21 Feb (JRC).

S Lecropt Carse: singles on 6 Feb; 27 Sep, 13 Oct, 3 and 17 Nov; 2 on 15 and 30 Dec (DT, DMB, DOE). Also: 1 Cambushinnie, Kinbuck 31 Mar (CJP); 1 L Watston, Doune 10 Nov (DOE); 2 Gart GPs, Callander 1 Dec (DOE); 3 Torrie, Callander 22 Dec (DA).

COMMON SNIPE *Gallinago gallinago* (B,W)

Inland WeBS: 37 in Jan, 36 in Feb, 67 in Mar, 8 in Sep, 28 in Oct, 115 in Nov and 117 in Dec.

F Winter/spring max: 3 Kinneil 20 Jan and 7 Apr. Summer: 2 Darnrig Moss 18 Jun. Autumn/winter max: 14 Skinflats 24 Aug; 3 Darnrig Moss 7 Nov.

C Nine Kennet Pans 12 Feb.

S Winter/spring max: 6 E Frew, Flanders Moss 17 Mar; 20 Killin, L Tay 5 Apr. Autumn/winter max: 6 Kirkton, Tyndrum 31 Oct; 7 Lecropt Carse 17 Nov; 18 Gart GPs, Callander 1 Dec.

EURASIAN WOODCOCK *Scolopax rusticola* (B, W)

F Three Torwood 15 Jan (AB). 1 Skinflats 15 Mar (GG). 2 Kinneil 28 Mar (RS). Singles Darnrig Moss 7 and 11 Nov (NB, RD). 1 Kinneil 1 Dec. 3 Langlees, Falkirk 7 Dec

(SPM).

S Max: Torrie, Callander 22 Dec. Records from: Stirling; BoA; Dunblane; Doune; Callander; Aberfoyle.

BLACK-TAILED GODWIT *Limosa limosa* (W)

Forth Est WeBS: 43 in Jan, 157 in Feb, 17 in Mar, 911 in Sep, 346 in Oct, 364 in Nov and 101 in Dec.

F Winter/spring max: 70 S Alloa 1 Feb; 163 Skinflats 28 Nov; 190 Kinneil 1 May. Autumn/winter max: 1185 Kinneil 1 Oct; 220 Skinflats 28 Nov.

C Max: 194 Kennet Pans 12 Apr.

BAR-TAILED GODWIT *Limosa lapponica* (W)

Forth Est WeBS: 227 in Jan, 187 in Feb, 88 in Mar, 19 in Sep, 11 in Oct, 35 in Nov and 251 in Dec.

F Winter/spring max: 70 Dunmore 30 Jan; 332 Kinneil 22 Jan; 17 Skinflats 15 Apr. Autumn/winter max: 9 Blackness 1 Oct; 15 Skinflats 8 Oct; 248 Kinneil 15 Dec.

C Max: 108 Kennet Pans 12 Feb.

WHIMBREL *Numenius phaeopus* (p)

F Spring: singles at Kinneil in Apr on 13th, 24th and 26th, and 1 May (CJP, DMB, RS); 1 Skinflats 23 Apr (GG); 1 Plean 1 May (DOE); 3 Skinflats 12 May (DOE). Autumn: 1 Kinneil 31 Jul (DMB) and 1 Skinflats 2 Aug (AB); Aug max of 4 Skinflats 23rd (DMB) and 6 Kinneil 25th (RS); 2 Kinneil 3 Sep (RS); last at Kinneil on 7 Sep and at Skinflats on 8 Sep.

C One Alloa Inch 27 Apr; 5 there 15 May (JRC). 52 Tullibody Inch 30 Apr (DMB). Singles Blackdevon Wetland 9 May and Kennet Pans 14 Jul (DMB).

EURASIAN CURLEW *Numenius arquata* (B, W)

Forth Est WeBS: 681 in Jan, 884 in Feb, 889 in Mar, 1067 in Sep, 452 in Oct, 585 in Nov and 865 in Dec.

Inland WeBS: 0 in Jan, 86 in Feb, 345 in Mar, 27 in Sep, 51 in Oct, 59 in Nov and 2 in Dec.

F Winter/spring max: 329 Skinflats 13 Jan. Autumn/winter max: 200 Kinneil 20 Sep; 385 Skinflats 15 Dec; 150 Blackness 28 Dec.

C Winter/spring max: 295 Tullibody Inch 29 Jan; 33 Cambus 2 Feb. Autumn/winter max: 167 Kennet Pans 22 Sep; 56 Cambus 21 Nov.

S Eighty-five Lecropt Carse 17 Mar.

COMMON SANDPIPER *Tringa hypoleucos* (B)

F First of year at Carronshore on 20 Apr (AE). Max: 5 Gart GPs, Callander 16 Jun. Elsewhere, up to 4 recorded in summer at Blairdrummond GPs, plus also at: Callander; BoD; Doune; Dunblane; Ashfield; Killin; Tyndrum. Last of year at L Coulter on 10 Sep.

C Up to 2 recorded in summer at Gartmorn Dam and Kennet Pans.

S First of year: singles at G Dochart and Killin, L Tay on 20 Apr (JPH). Up to 2 recorded in summer at Kinneil, Skinflats and Carronshore. Last of year at Blackness on 8 Sep.

*GREEN SANDPIPER *Tringa ochropus* (w, p)

F Singles at Gilston, Polmont 5 Jan to 4 Apr, with 2 on 14 Feb (RS, RTW). 1 Darnrig Moss 17 Jul (RD). Single Skinflats 10 Aug to 31 Aug (AB, GG, DOE). Singles at Gilston, Polmont 19 Aug to 31 Dec (RS).

C Singles Cambus 18 Aug (PMA) and 27 Sep (DMB).

S One Gart GPs, Callander 18 Aug (NB). Singles Blairdrummond GPs 25 Aug to 21 Sep, with 2 on 27 Aug (DOE).

*SPOTTED REDSHANK *Tringa erythropus* (p)

F Kinneil: Mar max of 2 on 27th; singles in Apr up to 6th; Aug max of 4 on 25th; and singles throughout Sep (RS, CJP, DMB, DT *et al.*).

COMMON GREENSHANK *Tringa nebularia* (w, p)

F Skinflats: singles in Jan, Feb, Mar; up to 2 in Aug; up to 2 in Sep; singles in Nov; up to 2 in Dec. Kinneil: singles in Jan, Feb, Mar, Apr, Jun, Jul; up to 2 in Aug; up to 3 in Sep; up to 4 in Oct; singles in Nov; up to 4 in Dec.

S Two Killin marshes 18 Apr (JPH).

COMMON REDSHANK *Tringa totanus* (B, W)

Forth Est WeBS: 1338 in Jan, 1287 in Feb, 931 in Mar, 1646 in Sep, 1638 in Oct, 1237 in Nov and 1201 in Dec.

F Winter/spring max: 683 Skinflats 13 Jan; 200 Kinneil 5 May. Autumn/winter max: 50 Blackness 8 Sep; 899 Kinneil 22 Sep; 723 Skinflats 20 Oct.

S Two Craigton Fm, Ashfield 23 Mar (CJP).

RUDDY TURNSTONE *Arenaria interpres* (W)

Forth Est WeBS: 1 in Jan, 13 in Feb, 8 in Mar, 2 in Sep, 4 in Oct, 6 in Nov and 3 in Dec.

F Ten Grangepans 22 Jan (DMB). 7 Grangemouth (MVB) and 6 Kinneil (JRC) 10 Feb. 1 Blackness 5 Aug (ACC). 11 Carriden 14 Oct (DMB). 3 Blackness 14 Oct (DMB). 5 Bo'ness 9 Nov (PM). One Grangemouth 15 Dec (MVB).

*ARCTIC SKUA *Stercorarius parasiticus* (p)

F Singles at Kinneil 24 Aug (CJP) and 29 Aug (RS), Bo'ness 7 Sep (GG), and Kinneil 14 and 28 Sep (CJP).

*LONG-TAILED SKUA *Stercorarius longicaudus* (p)

S One ad Earlsburn Resv 25 Jun for 20 minutes, before flying off SW (DB).

*GREAT SKUA *Stercorarius skua* (p)

F One Blackness 20 Sep (DMB). 1 Kinneil 29 Sep (CJP).

*BLACK-LEGGED KITTIWAKE *Rissa tridactyla* (P, w)

F Ten Bo'ness 23 Mar (GG), and 1 there (CJP) and 6 Kinneil on 24th (DT). 8 Bo'ness 8 Apr (GG). 1 found dead Blackness 12 Apr (LDF). 2 Kinneil 29 Dec (AB).

C One Gartmorn Dam 23 Mar (JRC).

S One 1w Lake of Menteith 12 to 14 Apr (RTW).

BLACK-HEADED GULL *Larus ridibundus* (B,W)

Inland WeBS: 571 in Jan, 732 in Feb, 1017 in Mar, 612 in Sep, 1202 in Oct, 1132 in Nov and 2013 in Dec.

Forth Est WeBS: 902 in Jan, 642 in Feb, 719 in Mar, 537 in Sep, 293 in Oct, 225 in Nov and 407 in Dec.

F Max: 200 Blackness 8 Sep; 250 Kinneil 17 Sep; 2500 Skinflats 8 Oct.

C Max: 340 Tullibody Inch 27 Feb; 109 Cambus 29 Mar; 142 Blackdevon Wetlands 29 Dec.

S Max: 350 Blairdrummond GPs 3 Mar; 200 L Watston, Doune 13 Oct; 200 Lecropt Carse 30 Dec.

*LITTLE GULL *Larus minutus* (p)

F One Kinneil 24 Mar (CJP, DT). 1 Carronshore 18 Aug (AE).

*MEDITERRANEAN GULL *Larus melanocephalus* (w)

F One 1w Kinneil 14 to 29 Sep (CJP), plus Skinflats 16 Sep (DOE) and Blackness 21 Sep (RTW). Ad Skinflats 7 Oct (GG). 1w Skinflats 3 and 6 Nov (DOE, AB).

C One 2w Kennet Pans 2 Aug (DMB).

COMMON GULL *Larus canus* (B,W)

Inland WeBS: 339 in Jan, 426 in Feb, 288 in Mar, 369 in Sep, 717 in Oct, 531 in Nov and 510 in Dec.

Forth Est WeBS: 206 in Jan, 111 in Feb, 150 in Mar, 106 in Sep, 38 in Oct, 87 in Nov and 307 in Dec.

F Max: 1500 Skinflats 8 Oct.

C Max: 30 Gartmorn Dam 4 Jun and 8 Oct.

S Max: 200 Blairdrummond 20 Jan; 79 Gart GPs, Callander 6 Oct.

*RING-BILLED GULL *Larus delawarensis*

F Ad Kinneil 3 Jan (JRC) and 6 Aug to 12 Nov (DT, CJP *et al.*); returning bird since 2007.

LESSER BLACK-BACKED GULL *Larus fuscus* (b, S)

Inland WeBS: 2 in Jan, 15 in Feb, 332 in Mar, 271 in Sep, 319 in Oct, 61 in Nov and 27 in Dec.

Forth Est WeBS: 1 in Jan, 3 in Feb, 28 in Mar, 17 in Sep, 8 in Oct, 4 in Nov and 5 in Dec.

F Max: 50 Kinneil 17 Sep; 60 Skinflats 7 Oct; 50 Bo'ness 9 Nov.

C Max: 50 Gartmorn Dam 4 Jun; 10 Cambus 18 Aug.

S Max: 28 Lake of Menteith 13 Mar; 70 Lecropt Carse 20 May; 40 L Watston, Doune 13 Oct.

HERRING GULL *Larus argentatus* (b, W)

Inland WeBS: 27 in Jan, 40 in Feb, 62 in Mar, 46 in Sep, 30 in Oct, 113 in Nov and 65 in Dec.

Forth Est WeBS: 146 in Jan, 185 in Feb, 222 in Mar, 376 in Sep, 174 in Oct, 104 in Nov and 257 in Dec.

F Max: 200 Skinflats 16 Sep; 250 Kinneil 17 Sep.

C Max: 26 Gartmorn Dam 23 Mar.

S Max: 30 Lake of Menteith 1 Jan; 30 Dunblane 25 Apr.

GREAT BLACK-BACKED GULL *Larus marinus* (S,W)

Inland WeBS: 4 in Jan, 6 in Feb, 1 in Mar, 6 in Sep, 7 in Oct, 7 in Nov and 6 in Dec.

Forth Est WeBS: 9 in Jan, 2 in Feb, 2 in Mar, 0 in Sep, 3 in Oct, 1 in Nov and 9 in Dec.

F Max: 15 Kinneil 17 Sep; 15 Skinflats 8 Oct.

C Max: 2 Tullibody Inch 29 Jan.

S Max: 3 Lecropt Carse 20 Jan; 3 Gart GPs, Callander 25 May.

*BLACK TERN *Chlidonias niger* (p)

F One Kinneil 7 and 8 Sep (AB).

SANDWICH TERN *Sterna sandvicensis* (s, P)

F First of year: 1 Kincardine Br 20 May (ACC). Max: 40 Blackness and 30 Bo'ness 8 Sep. Last of year: 3 Blackness 14 Oct (DMB).

COMMON TERN *Sterna hirundo* (S)

F First of year: 1 Kinneil 18 May (CJP). Max: 10 Blackness 5 Aug; 10 Kinneil 31 Aug.

S One Lake of Menteith 8 Jul (RTW).

*ARCTIC TERN *Sterna paradisaea* (s)

F 14 Skinflats 24 Aug (RTW). Kinneil: 2 on 24 Aug, 26 Aug and 30 Aug, and 1 on 30 Sep (DOE, DT, CJP).

S One Lake of Menteith 16 and 17 Apr (RTW).

PUFFIN *Fratercula arctica* (p)

F One picked up dead Blackness 10 Apr (LDF).

*RAZORBILL *Alca torda* (s, w)

F Four Bo'ness 23 Mar (GG), and 6 there (CJP) and Skinflats (GG) on 24th. 9 picked up dead Blackness 8 Apr (LDF).

C Eleven Cambus 24 Mar (JRC).

*GUILLEMOT *Uria aalge* (s, w)

F Kinneil: 1 on 10 Mar and 4 on 24th (JRC, DT). Bo'ness: 9 on 23 Mar, 3 on 24th and 1 on 25th (GG, CJP).

C Five Cambus 24 Mar (JRC).

S One Cableland, Aberfoyle 25 Mar (DOE).

LITTLE AUK Alle Alle (p)

F One Kinneil 10 Mar (JRC).

FERAL PIGEON *Columba livia* (B,W)
BBS: recorded at 1.1 b/lkm (2004-2013 average: 1.1 b/lkm).
F Max: 400 Skinflats 13 Jan.
S Max: 30 Lecropt Carse 17 Nov.

STOCK DOVE *Columba oenas* (B, W)
F Max: 10 S Alloa 1 Feb; 6 Kinneil 5 May; 12 Skinflats 12 May; 14 Skinflats Tidal Exchange 21 Dec.
C Max: 20 Cambus 18 Feb. Also recorded Menstrie Glen.
S Max: 12 Lecropt Carse 17 Mar; 7 Holmehill, Dunblane 16 Feb; 16 L Watston, Doune 16 Mar; 15 Blairdrummond GPs 24 Nov.

WOODPIGEON *Columba palumbus* (B, W)
BBS: recorded at 3.7 b/lkm (2004-2013 average: 3.9 b/lkm).
F Max: 200 Skinflats 5 Jan; 100 S Alloa 1 Feb; 50 Carronshore 23 Mar; 70 Kinneil 26 Aug.
C Max: 100 Tullibody Inch 29 Jan; 100 Cambus 18 Feb; 50 Gartmorn Dam 16 Sep; 50 Alva 22 Sep.
S Max: 800 Kinbuck 20 Mar; 200 Lanrick, Doune 10 Nov; 150 Lecropt Carse and 101 Holme Hill, Dunblane 17 Nov; 400 Blairdrummond GPs 5 Dec.

EURASIAN COLLARED DOVE *Streptopelia decaocto* (B, W)
Recorded throughout region. BBS: recorded at 0.3 b/lkm (2004-2013 average: 0.3 b/lkm).
S Max: 22 Blairdrummond GPs 10 Nov.

COMMON CUCKOO *Cuculus canorus* (B)
First spring record: 1 Falkirk 19 Apr (BP) was within 5 year range (15 to 27 April).
C Single Alva Glen 21 and 26 May (PMA).
S Max: 4 G Lochay 18 May (JPH). Also recorded: Touch; BoD; Callander; L Venachar; Strathyre; Flanders Moss; Lake of Menteith; Brig O' Turk; G Finglas; G Dochart; L Katrine; Tyndrum.

BARN OWL *Tyto alba* (b, w)
S Recorded from: Stirling; Aberfoyle; Killin and Tyndrum.

TAWNY OWL *Strix aluco* (B, W)
S Recorded from: BoA; Dunblane; BoD; Doune; Aberfoyle; and Killin.

LONG-EARED OWL *Asio otus* (b, w)
F One pr and 1 Y near Bo'ness 20 May (TG).
C One Alva 12 Dec (KB).
S One pr and 2-3 Y calling BoD 2 Jul (KD). One pr and 1 Y Kinbuck 10 Jul (AHa).

SHORT-EARED OWL *Asio flammeus* (b, W)
F Singles Kinneil 5 Jan to 1 May (TG, CJP, RD *et al.*). 1 Skinflats 24 Apr (RD).
S One pr Touch 10 Mar (DBr).

COMMON SWIFT *Apus apus* (B)
Recorded throughout region. BBS: recorded at 0.2 b/lkm (2004-2013 average: 0.5 b/lkm).
Spring arrival: 1 Skinflats 24 Apr was earlier than past 8 year range (27 April to 4 May).
F Max: 31 Bo'ness 1 Aug.
S Max: 60 Lake of Menteith 28 Apr; 50 Doune 27 Jul; 50 Dunblane 28 Jul; 60 BoA 30 Jul.

COMMON KINGFISHER *Alcedo atthis* (b, w)
F Recorded from Lecropt Carse; Dunblane; Ashfield; Blairdrummond GPs; Doune; Gart GPs, Callander; Callander; Lake of Menteith; L Lubhair; G Dochart; and Tyndrum.
C Recorded from Cambus.
S Recorded from: Skinflats Tidal Exchange; Skinflats; Kinneil; Larbert; and Falkirk.

EUROPEAN GREEN WOODPECKER *Picus viridis* (B, W)
C Recorded from: Menstrie Glen; Alva; Dollar; and Gartmorn Dam.
S Recorded from: BoD; L Venachar; Aberfoyle; and G Lochay.

GREAT SPOTTED WOODPECKER *Dendrocopos major* (B, W)
F Recorded from Bo'ness.
C Recorded from Alva.
S Recorded from: Dunblane; BoD; Blairdrummond GPs; Callander; Lake of Menteith; and G Dochart.

SKYLARK *Alauda arvensis* (B, W)
BBS: recorded at 1.7 b/lkm (2004-2013 average: 1.7 b/lkm).
F Max: 55 Higgin's Neuk 28 Nov; 30 Skinflats 15 Dec.
C Max: 50 Gartmorn Dam 20 Oct.
S Max: 19 Ashfield 19 Jan; 105 Lecropt Carse 1 Mar; 20 Kirkton, Tyndrum 12 Apr.

SAND MARTIN *Riparia riparia* (B)
BBS: recorded at 0.2 b/lkm (2004-2013 average: 0.5 b/lkm).
First spring record of 25 Lake of Menteith 11 Apr was later than previous 8 year range: 4 to 30 Mar.
F Max: 50 Carronshore 4 May; 80 Skinflats 12 May.
C 50 Gartmorn Dam 14 May.
S Max: 70 Blairdrummond GPs 14 Apr; 450 Lake of Menteith 17 Apr.

BARN SWALLOW *Hirundo rustica* (B)
BBS: recorded at 2.4 b/lkm (2004-2013 average: 2.5 b/lkm).
First spring record of 1 Skinflats 13 Apr was later than previous 8 year range: 6 Mar to 6 Apr.
F Max: 400 Skinflats and 60 Blackness 8 Sep.
C Max: 40 Gartmorn Dam 14 May.
S Max: 275 Lake of Menteith 17 Apr; 50 L Watston 28 Aug; 350 Blairdrummond GPs 21 Sep.

COMMON HOUSE MARTIN *Delichon urbica* (B)
BBS: recorded at 0.6 b/lkm (2004-2013 average: 0.8 b/lkm).
First spring record of 2 Blairdrummond GPs 14 Apr (DOE) was towards end of 8 year range: 6 to 16 Apr.
F Max: Carronshore 4 May.
S Max: 90 Lake of Menteith 17 Apr; 400 Blairdrummond GPs 21 Sep.

TREE PIPIT *Anthus trivialis* (B)
First spring record of 1 Duchray Castle, Aberfoyle 19 Apr (RE) was within the 8 year range: 12 to 27 Apr.
F Singles at Skinflats on 26 and 30 Apr, and 7 May, with 2 there 9 Sep (DMB, GG, RS).
C One singing Menstrie Glen 17 May (KD).
S Max: 5 Balquhidder Station 2 May (RB); 10 AOT Tyndrum 10 May (DMB); 6 G Dochart 19 May (JPH); 2-3 AOT nr BoA 16 Jun (CJP). Also recorded from: Blairdrummond GPs; Dunblane; BoD; Doune; Callander; Kilmahog; Brig o' Turk; Flanders Moss; Lake of Menteith; Aberfoyle; L Chon; L Achray; G Lochay; G Beich; and Crianlarich.

MEADOW PIPIT *Anthus pratensis* (B, W)
BBS: recorded at 4.6 b/lkm (2004-2013 average: 4.7 b/lkm).
F Max: 200 Skinflats 9 Sep.
S Max: 300 Kirkton, Tyndrum 18 Apr; 60 Drumloist, BoD 21 Apr; 65 L Watston, Doune 25 Apr; 150 Gart GPs, Callander 8 Sep.

*EURASIAN ROCK PIPIT *Anthus petrosus* (w)
F Two Skinflats 6 Jan (GG). 1 Skinflats Tidal Exchange 27 Jan (AB). 3 S Alloa 1 Feb (DMB).
C One Longcarse, Alloa 21 Feb; with 2 there 7 and 31 Dec (JRC).

*YELLOW WAGTAIL *Motacilla flava*
F Two Skinflats 10 May (AB).
GREY WAGTAIL *Motacilla cinerea* (B, w)
C Recorded at Gartmorn Dam.
S Max: 4 pr Allanwater, Dunblane 6 Apr; 10 Killin marshes 21 Sep. Also recorded at: Airthrey, BoA; Dunblane; Blairdrummond GPs; BoD; and Tyndrum.
PIED WAGTAIL *Motacilla alba yarrellii* (B, w)
BBS: recorded at 0.2 b/lkm (2004-2013 average: 0.4 b/lkm).
F Max: 26 S Alloa 1 Feb; 20 Skinflats 26 Apr; 20 Darnrig Moss 30 Oct. White wagtail *M.a.alba*, max: 30 Skinflats 28 Apr.
C Max: 16 Tullibody Inch 30 Apr.
S Max: 100 at Stirling train station roost 7 Feb (CRe); 20 Kirkton, Tyndrum 13 Sep.
BOHEMIAN WAXWING *Bombycilla garrulus* (w)
Birds continued to be present from 2012.
F Jan: 8 Bo'ness 2 Jan; max of 12 Falkirk on 23rd. Feb: max of 57 Larbert on 9th. Mar: 6 Carron 21st; max of 40 Falkirk on 24th. Apr: 12 Larbert 2 Apr; max of 30 Falkirk on 18th (and last record).
C Three Fishcross 2 Feb. 20 Dollar 18 Mar.
S Jan: max of 21 BoA on 1st; max of 8 Dunblane on 13th; 25 Stirling 14th. Feb: max of 30 Dunblane on 2nd; 1 Killin 8th; max of 30 Stirling on 11th. Mar: max of 15 Stirling 4th; 10 Dunblane 12th. 6 Stirling 11 Apr.
In Nov: 2 Airthrey, BoA 6th; 3 Callander 13th; 1 Auchtertyre, Tyndrum 22nd.
WHITE-THROATED DIPPER *Cinclus cinclus* (B, W)
F Recorded from: R Carron in Larbert and Denny.
C Recorded from: Cambus; Alva; Dollar.
S Max: 4 pr Dunblane 6 Apr. Also recorded from: BoA; Blairdrummond GPs; Ashfield; Doune; Callander; Aberfoyle; Killin; Balquhidder Glen; G Lochay; Crianlarich; and Tyndrum.
WINTER WREN *Troglodytes troglodytes* (B, W)
Widespread and common. BBS: recorded at 1.9 b/lkm (2004-2013 average: 1.9 b/lkm).
F Max: 11 Carriden 24 Apr.
C Max: 12 Gartmorn Dam 14 May.
S Max: 12 Drumloist, BoD 21 Apr; 11 Holmehill, Dunblane 18 May; 10 Lanrick, Doune 20 Oct; 14 Blairdrummond GPs 9 Nov.
DUNNOCK *Prunella modularis* (B, W)
Widespread and common. BBS: recorded at 0.3 b/lkm (2004-2013 average: 0.6 b/lkm).
S Max: 11 Holmehill, Dunblane 29 Mar.
EUROPEAN ROBIN *Erithacus rubecula* (B,W)
Widespread and common. BBS: recorded at 1.2 b/lkm (2004-2013 average: 1.2 b/lkm).
F Max: 10 Carriden 25 Apr.
C Max: 14 Gartmorn Dam 8 Oct.
S Max: 17 Holmehill, Dunblane 26 Jan; 15 Drumloist, BoD 21 Apr; 24 Balquhidder 15 Oct; 23 Airthrey, BoA 24 Oct.
COMMON REDSTART *Phoenicurus phoenicurus* (B)
First spring record of 1 Killin marshes 20 Apr (JPH) was within the 8 year range: 12 to 27 Apr.
F Two Skinflats 14 Jul and 25 Aug, and single 20-23 Aug (AB, PB, GG, RTW).
S Max: 4 Flanders Moss 2 May; 10 AOT Tyndrum 10 May; 6 G Lochay 18 May; 4 G Dochart 19 May. Also recorded from: Sheriffmuir; BoD; Doune; Callander; Brig o' Turk; Lake of Menteith; Thornhill; Aberfoyle; Killin; and Balquhidder Station.

WHINCHAT *Saxicola rubetra* (B)

First spring record of 2 Gleann Meann 30 Apr (NW) was within the previous 8 year range: 24 April to 2 May.

F Singles Skinflats 11 Mar and 24 Aug. Two Strathavon Fm, Slamannan 18 Jun. 1 Kinneil 8 Aug.

C One Dollar Glen 3 Jul. 1 Garnel Burn, Tillicoultry 13 Jul.

S Max: 6 G Dochart 19 May. Also recorded from: Sheriffmuir; Doune; Lochearnhead; G Lochay; Tyndrum.

EURASIAN STONECHAT *Saxicola torquata* (b, w)

This species is still recovering from the cold winters of 2009 and 2010.

F One Gardrum Moss 13 Nov.

C One Blackdevon Wetlands 14 Apr.

S Single pairs recorded at: BoD and Flanders Moss. Also recorded (up to 2) from: Buchlyvie and Tyndrum.

NORTHERN WHEATEAR *Oenanthe oenanthe* (B)

First spring record of 1 Tyndrum 8 Apr was later than the previous 8 year range: 21 Mar to 6 Apr.

F Max: 13 Kinneil 16 Apr; 8 Skinflats 27 Apr.

C One Alva 27 Apr (AE).

S Max: 9 Drumloist, BoD 21 Apr; 8 Cromlix, BoD 27 Apr; 7 Flanders Moss 2 May.

*RING OUZEL *Turdus torquatus* (b)

S Two Dumyat 6 Apr (BD). 1 Auchtertyre, Tyndrum 19 Apr (JPH). 1 Stob Binnein 5 Jun (JRC). 1 imm Cam Chreag 6 Jul (JPH). 1 pr Coire Luaidh 13 Jul (JPH). 1 Ben a Chroin 27 Jul (EC). 1 imm Ben Each, G Ample 7 Aug (RE).

COMMON BLACKBIRD *Turdus merula* (B, W)

Widespread and common. BBS: recorded at 2.3 b/lkm (2004-2013 average: 2.3 b/lkm).

C Max: 23 Gartmorn Dam 4 Dec; 15 Alva 14 Dec.

S Max: 15 Blairdrummond GPs 20 Jan; 17 Holmehill, Dunblane 18 May

FIELDFARE *Turdus pilaris* (W)

Last spring record of 1 Ashfield 21 Apr (CJP) was within the previous 8 year range: 25 Mar to 14 May.

First autumn record of 1 Skinflats 10 Oct (PB) was within the previous 8 year range: 3 Sep to 22 Oct.

F Max: 200 Larbert 25 Mar; 300 Skinflats 3 Nov; 500 S Alloa 10 Dec.

S Max: 1000 Kirkton, Tyndrum 22 Oct; 600 Auchinlay, Dunblane 26 Oct; 350 Lecropt Carse 3 Nov.

SONG THRUSH *Turdus philomelos* (B, W)

Widespread. BBS: recorded at 0.4 b/lkm (2004-2013 average: 0.5 b/lkm).

S Max: 12 Kirkton, Tyndrum 21 Mar; 12 Drumloist, BoD 21 Apr; 10 Blairdrummond GPs 5 May.

REDWING *Turdus iliacus* (W)

Last spring record of 1 G Dochart 20 Apr (JPH) was earlier the previous 8 year range: 7 Mar to 1 May.

First autumn record of 1 Kirkton, Tyndrum 3 Oct (JPH) was within the previous 8 year range: 27 Sep to 12 Oct.

F Max: 60 Falkirk 29 Oct.

S Max: 1000 G Dochart 13 Oct; 130 Dunblane 16 Oct; 115 Lake of Menteith 23 Oct; 100 Airthrey, BoA 6 Nov.

MISTLE THRUSH *Turdus viscivorus* (B, W)

Widespread. BBS: recorded at 0.1 b/lkm (2004-2013 average: 0.2 b/lkm).

S Max: 12 Kirkton, Tyndrum 21 Mar.

COMMON GRASSHOPPER WARBLER *Locustella naevia* (b)

First spring record of 1 Laighhills, Dunblane 22 Apr (CJP) was within the previous 8 year range: 17 to 27 Apr.

F Up to 2 singing M at: Kinneil; Skinflats; Darnrig Moss; and Torwood.

C One Dollar Glen 3 Jul.

S Two singing M Gart GPs, Callander 5 May. Single singing M also at: Flanders Moss; Lake of Menteith; and Killin, L Tay.

SEDGE WARBLER *Acrocephalus schoenobaenus* (B)

First spring record of 1 Skinflats 26 Apr (GG) was within the previous 8 year range: 21 to 31 Apr.

F Max: 21 singing M Skinflats 21 May.

C Max: 4 Cambus 12 May.

S Max: 4 Blairdrummond GPs.

*REED WARBLER *Acrocephalus scirpaceus*

Breeding of the species in the Upper Forth area was first confirmed in 2011.

F One Kinneil 27 Apr (CJP). Successfully bred at Skinflats, present from 27 Apr to 8 Sep (RTW, AB, GG *et al.*). These are the 9th to 10th records of the species in the recording area.

EURASIAN BLACKCAP *Sylvia atricapilla* (B)

First spring record: of 1 BoA 23 Mar (MVB) was either wintering bird or earlier than previous 8 year range: 1-13 Apr.

F Max: 17 M and 3 F Skinflats 26 Apr.

C Max: 8 Gartmorn Dam 4 Jun.

S Winter: 1 BoA 25 Jan. Max: 15 Blairdrummond GPs 5 May; 6 Holmehill, Dunblane 25 Jun.

GARDEN WARBLER *Sylvia borin* (B)

First spring record of 1 Dunblane 30 Apr (CJP) was within the previous 8 year range: 15 Apr to 2 May.

F Recorded from: Skinflats; Falkirk; Larbert; and Torwood.

C Max: 7 Gartmorn Dam 7 Jul. Also recorded from Alva.

S Recorded from: Stirling; Airthrey, BoA; Lecropt Carse; Dunblane; Cromlix, BoD; Rosehall, BoD; Blairdrummond GPs; Bucklyvie; Gart GPs, Callander; Kilmahog; Brig o' Turk; Lake of Menteith; G Dochart; and G Lochay.

COMMON WHITETHROAT *Sylvia communis* (B)

BBS: recorded at 0.2 b/lkm (2004-2013 average: 0.2 b/lkm).

First spring record of 1 Stirling 9 Apr was earlier than the previous 8 year range: 20 Apr to 2 May.

F Max: 8 Skinflats and 5 Kinneil 24 Aug.

C Max: 5 Gartmorn Dam 14 May.

S Max: 6 Hill of Row, Dunblane 24 Aug.

WOOD WARBLER *Phylloscopus sibilatrix* (B)

First spring record of 1 Tigh Mor, L Achray 28 Apr was within the previous 8 year range: 17 Apr to 5 May.

S Max: 3 Kilmahog 4 May; 6 Little Drum Wood, Brig o' Turk 2 Jun; 3 Pass of Leny, Callander 6 Jun. Also recorded from: Mine Wood, BoA; Callander Crags; Strathyre; Lake of Menteith; Aberfoyle; Killin; G Dochart; and G Lochay.

COMMON CHIFFCHAFF *Phylloscopus collybita* (B)

First spring record of 1 singing Kinneil 31 Mar (CJP) was at end the previous 8 year range: 13 to 31 Mar.

F Max: 5 Carriden, Bo'ness 25 Apr.

S Max: 9 Blairdrummond GPs 5 May.

WILLOW WARBLER *Phylloscopus trochilus* (B)

BBS: recorded at 1.7 b/lkm (2004-2013 average: 1.5 b/lkm). First spring records of 3 BoA (DMB) and 2 Lake of Menteith (RTW) 18 Apr were later than the previous 8 year range: 3-14 Apr.

F Max: 50 Skinflats and 12 Kinneil curling pond 16 Apr.

C Max: 20 Gartmorn Dam 6 Aug.

S Max: 31 Touch and 25 Blairdrummond 5 May; 15 Drumloist, BoD 18 May.

GOLDCREST *Regulus regulus* (B, W)

BBS: recorded at 0.4 b/lkm (2004-2013 average: 0.5 b/lkm).

F Max: 10 Skinflats 26 Sep.

S Max: 16 Ben A'an 12 Oct; 14 Lanrick, Doune 10 Nov; 15 Blairdrummond GPs 24 Nov.

SPOTTED FLYCATCHER *Muscicapa striata* (B)

First spring record of 1 Flanders Moss 2 May (DOE) was earlier than the previous 8 year range: 9 to 20 May.

F Max: 4 Skinflats 24 Aug. Also recorded Larbert House.

C Max: 4 Alva woodland park 28 Jul.

S Max: 6 Airthrey, BoA 21 Aug; 5 L Rusky 5 Nov. Also recorded: Blairdrummond GPs; Dunblane; Cromlix, BoD; Bracklinn, Callander; Brig o' Turk; Flanders Moss; Lake of Menteith; Killin; G Lochay; G Dochart; and Tyndrum.

EURASIAN PIED FLYCATCHER *Ficedula hypoleuca* (b)

S Three G Lochay 18 May (JPH).

BEARDED TIT

C One pair bred at a confidential location, with at least 2 juv recorded (JRC, DMB). This is the 2nd record of the species for the recorded area following the record below.

2012: 1m and 1f Skinflats 28 Dec (DG, KW).

LONG-TAILED TIT *Aegithalos caudatus* (B, W)

Widespread. BBS: recorded at 0.1 b/lkm (2004-2013 average: 0.1 b/lkm).

F Max: 15 Skinflats 7 Jan; 11 Falkirk 7 Dec.

C Max: 12 R Devon, Clackmannan 3 Feb; 10 Cambus 17 Nov.

S Max: 16 Holmehill, Dunblane 24 Nov; 16 Blairdrummond GPs 28 Dec; 17 Lake of Menteith 29 Dec.

BLUE TIT *Cyanistes caeruleus* (B, W)

Widespread. BBS: recorded at 1.7 b/lkm (2004-2013 average: 1.8 b/lkm).

C Max: 20 Castlebridge business park, Clackmannan 2 Apr.

S Max: 22 Holmehill, Dunblane 24 Nov.

GREAT TIT *Parus major* (B, W)

Widespread. BBS: recorded at 0.9 b/lkm (2004-2013 average: 1.0 b/lkm).

C Max: 20 Castlebridge business park, Clackmannan 2 Apr.

S Max: 21 Holmehill, Dunblane 26 Jan.

COAL TIT *Periparus ater* (B, W)

Widespread. BBS: recorded at 0.3 b/lkm (2004-2013 average: 0.5 b/lkm).

S Max: 12 Blairdrummond GPs 14 Dec.

EURASIAN NUTHATCH *Sitta europaea*

After the first record in 1999 and first breeding recorded in 2009, the species is spreading particularly in Stirlingshire.

F One Callendar Park, Falkirk 17-18 Feb. One Carriden, Bo'ness 25 Apr.

C One Dollar Glen 1 Jun.

S Max: 4 Blairdrummond GPs May and Aug. Also recorded in: Stirling; BoA; Dunblane (Holmehill, Kippenross, Ledcammeroch, Keir); Doune castle; Lanrick, Doune; Callander; Kilmahog; Brig o'Turk; Lake of Menteith; Aberfoyle; and L Katrine.

EURASIAN TREECREEPER *Certhia familiaris* (B, W)
Widespread in small numbers.
S Max: 6 Airthrey, BoA 31 Jul.

EURASIAN JAY *Garrulus glandarius* (B, W)
Widespread in small numbers.
F Max: 5 Torwood 14 Nov.
C Max: 4 Gartmorn Dam 8 Oct.
S Max: 9 Lanrick, Doune 20 Oct.

EURASIAN MAGPIE *Pica pica* (B, W)
Widespread in Falkirk and Clackmannan districts, and Stirling area.
BBS: recorded at 0.4 b/lkm (2004-2013 average: 0.5 b/lkm).
F Max: 25 Union Canal, Falkirk 18 Jan.
C Max: 19 Alva 22 Sep
S Max: 14 Longleys, BoA 24 Jan; 25 Stockbridge, Dunblane 22 Feb; 11 Holmehill, Dunblane 12 Oct. Also recorded from Fallin and Kirkton, Tyndrum.

WESTERN JACKDAW *Corvus monedula* (B, W)
BBS: recorded at 2.5 b/lkm (2004-2013 average: 2.7 b/lkm).
F Max: 140 Skinflats 5 Jan; 200 Carronshore 8 Jul.
S Max: 100 Buchany 6 Jan; 380 BoA 13 Mar; 300 Lecropt carse 17 Mar; 300 Blairdrummond GPs 21 Sep.

ROOK *Corvus frugilegus* (B, W)
BBS: recorded at 3.7 b/lkm (2004-2013 average: 3.1 b/lkm).
F Max: 250 Skinflats 20 Jan; 150 Falkirk 22 Nov.
S Breeding: 296 nests Dunblane in Apr, up 25 compared to 2012 (MVB).

CARRION CROW *Corvus corone* (B, W)
BBS: recorded at 3.4 b/lkm (2004-2013 average: 3.5 b/lkm).
F Max: 50 Bo'ness 9 Nov; 76 Skinflats 28 Nov.
C Max: 80 Gartmorn Dam 4 Jun; 60 Alva 22 Sep.
S Max: 49 Longleys, BoA 24 Jan.

HOODED CROW *Corvus cornix* (b, w)
S Widespread is western part of region. Recorded from: Argaty, BoD; Kippen; Aberfoyle; Balquhidder Glen; L Dochart; Crianlarich; and Tyndrum.

NORTHERN RAVEN *Corvus corax* (B, W)
F Two S Alloa 1 Feb. 2 Greencraig Fm, Callifornia 13 Nov.
C Three Tullibody Inch 22 Nov.
S Max: 12 Lanrick, Doune 17 Mar; 10 Drumloist, BoD 21 Apr; 14 Kirkton, Tyndrum 20 Aug. Also recorded from: Dunblane; Sheriffmuir; Doune; Aberfoyle; Beinn Each; Killin; G Dochart; Sgaith a'Chaise; and Tyndrum.

COMMON STARLING *Sturnus vulgaris* (B, W)
BBS: recorded at 5.3 b/lkm (2004-2013 average: 4.8 b/lkm).
F Max: 300 Skinflats 5 Jan.
C Max: 100 Cambus 18 Feb.
S Max: 100 Kinbuck 6 Feb; 140 Doune 22 Sep; 150 Craigforth, Stirling 21 Dec; 150 Flanders Moss 24 Dec.

HOUSE SPARROW *Passer domesticus* (B, W)
BBS: recorded at 1.8 b/lkm (2004-2013 average: 2.0 b/lkm).
F Max: 50 Skinflats 22 Sep.
C Max: 20 Gartmorn Dam 8 Oct.
S Max: 150 Kinbuck 18 Aug.

EURASIAN TREE SPARROW *Passer montanus* (B, W)
F Max: 60 Skinflats 6 Jan; 10 S Alloa 1 Feb; 10 Blackness 14 Oct; 15 Skinflats Tidal Exchange 20 Oct. Also recorded in Bo'ness.

C Max: 17 Alva 19 Jan; 20 Gartmorn Dam 6 Aug.

S Max: 40 Ashfield 2 Jan; 44 Barbush, Dunblane 3 Jan; 60 Craigforth, Stirling 5 Jan; 20 Glenhead, Dunblane 20 Feb; 31 Lecropt Carse 1 Mar; 30 Drip Moss 21 Nov; 41 Greenyards, Dunblane 31 Oct; 20 Frew, Flanders Moss 24 Dec.

CHAFFINCH *Fringilla coelebs* (B, W)

BBS: recorded at 4.0 b/lkm (2004-2013 average: 4.0 b/lkm).

C Max: 40 Alva 15 Dec.

F Max: 60 Skinflats Tidal Exchange 2 Feb; 91 Skinflats 7 Jan; 50 Torwood 15 Jan.

S Max: 130 Laighhills, Dunblane 1 Jan; 60 Blairdrummond GPs 2 Jan; 150 Greenyards, Dunblane 5 Jan; 550 Lecropt Carse 24 Jan; 200 Kinbuck 6 Feb; 150 W Cambushinnie 22 Nov; 190 Stonehill, Dunblane 26 Nov.

BRAMBLING *Fringilla montifringilla* (W)

F Winter/spring max: 40 Powfoulis 2 Jan; 100 Skinflats 3 Feb. Autumn/winter max: 8 Kinneil 3 Nov.

C Winter/spring max: 6 Alva 16 Jan; 24 Cambus 11 Mar. Autumn/winter max: 4 Gartmorn Dam 20 Oct.

S Winter/spring max: 97 Laighhills, Dunblane 1 Jan; 600 Greenyards, Dunblane and 50 Ashfield 5 Jan; 120 Lecropt Carse 24 Jan; 100 Glenhead, Dunblane 20 Feb. Autumn/winter max: 14 Blairdrummond GPs 27 Oct.

EUROPEAN GREENFINCH *Carduelis chloris* (B, W)

Widespread. BBS: recorded at 0.2 b/lkm (2004-2013 average: 0.6 b/lkm).

F Max: 30 Skinflats 23 Jan.

S Max: 45 Drip Moss 13 Jan.

EUROPEAN GOLDFINCH *Carduelis carduelis* (B, W)

BBS: recorded at 0.5 b/lkm (2004-2013 average: 0.5 b/lkm).

F Max: 70 Skinflats 1 Sep; 112 Airth 28 Nov; 70 Kincardine Br 15 Dec.

S Max: 65 Ashfield 6 Oct; 65 Ashfield 6 Oct.

EURASIAN SISKIN *Carduelis spinus* (B, W)

BBS: recorded at 0.4 b/lkm (2004-2013 average: 0.3 b/lkm).

F Max: 35 Bo'ness 12 Jan; 15 Carronshore 8 Apr.

C Max: 12 Gartmorn Dam 8 Oct; 12 Alva 15 Dec.

S Max: 40 Kippenross, Dunblane 21 Sep; 45 Blairdrummond GPs 27 Oct; 45 Invertrossachs, Callander 24 Nov.

COMMON LINNET *Carduelis cannabina* (B, W)

F Max: 30 Airth 16 Aug; 150 Skinflats 20 Dec.

S Max: 130 Cairnston, Dunblane 15 Mar; 120 Lecropt Carse and 70 Drip Moss 30 Dec.

TWITE *Carduelis flavirostris* (b, W)

F Three Airth 7 Jan (RTW). 3 Skinflats 10 Feb (GG). 8 Kincardine Br 16 Feb (AE). 3 Glensburgh, Grangemouth 6 Jul, with 3 there 26 Oct and 2 Nov (AE). 120 Airth 21-28 Nov (DMB, MVB). 3 Skinflats 7-21 Dec (DMB, PB, DOE). 1 Greencraig Farm, California 28 Dec (BCM).

C Five Longcarse, Alloa 9 Nov, with 14 there 7 Dec (JRC).

S Forty-five Lecropt Carse 19 Feb (DMB). Singles Stob Binnein 1 May and 1 Jun (JRC). Tyndrum: max of 3 in May, on 15th (JPH). 40 G Gyle 22 Dec (DOE).

LESSER REDPOLL *Acanthis cabaret* (b, W)

F Max: 9 Skinflats 3 Feb; 15 Falkirk 4 May; 8 Kinneil 28 Sep; 22 Darnrig 9 Dec.

C Max: 5 Gartmorn Dam 10 Nov.

S Max: 15 Dunblane 2 Jan; 11 Stirling 22 Apr; 30 Aberfoyle 17 Dec.

*COMMON REDPOLL *Acanthis flammea*

F One Skinflats 13 May (GG).

S One M BoA 13 May (DMB).

COMMON CROSSBILL *Loxia curvirostra* (b, W)
F Max: 2 Torwood 8 May.
S Max: 7 Ashfield 5 Jan; 5 Callander Crags 21 Jul; 24 Kirkton, Tyndrum 18 Oct; 13 L Lubhair 10 Nov; 25 Tyndrum 30 Nov. Also recorded from: Dunblane; Doune; Flanders Moss; and Ben A'an.
COMMON BULLFINCH *Pyrrhula pyrrhula* (B, W)
F Max: 6 Torwood 14 Nov.
C Max: 8 Gartmorn Dam 12 Jan.
S Max: 9 Ashfield 2 Jan; 6 Killin 1 Dec; 7 Doune 14 Dec.
HAWFINCH
S Two Kippen 2 Feb, with one still on 3rd (LL). This is the first record for Upper Forth since 1991.
SNOW BUNTING *Plectrophenax nivalis* (W)
S One > Dunblane 13 Jan (CJP). 20 Caol Ghleann, Tyndrum 19 Jan – 8 Feb, with 140 there 11 Feb (JPH). M singing Stob Binnein 1 May, and individual there 8 Jul (JRC).
YELLOWHAMMER *Emberiza citrinella* (B, W)
BBS: recorded at 0.5 b/lkm (2004-2013 average: 0.5 b/lkm).
F Max: 80 Skinflats 15 Dec.
C Max: 10 Cambus 18 Feb; 10 Alva 15 Dec.
S Max: 44 Greenyards, Dunblane 5 Jan; 45 Drip Moss 13 Jan; 47 Lecropt Carse 24 Jan.
REED BUNTING *Emberiza schoeniclus* (B, W)
BBS: recorded at 0.1 b/lkm (2004-2013 average: 0.2 b/lkm).
F Max: 95 Skinflats 12 Jan; 20 Glensburgh, Grangemouth 26 Oct.
C Max: 6 Cambus 18 Feb; 5 Alva 15 Dec.
S Max: 30 Kippenross 19 Jan; 142 Lecropt Carse 24 Jan.

ESCAPED SPECIES

RING-NECKED PARAKEET
S One Cambusbarron 9 Nov (KR).
BLACK SWAN
S One Lake of Menteith 26 May to 11 Aug (LDF, RTW).

RINGING REPORT

Ben Darvill

The following report highlights a selection of notable observations from bird ringing activities. For access to additional information, visit: http://www.bto.org/volunteer-surveys/ringing/publications/online-ringing-reports

A total of 4,182 birds were ringed in the 'Central' region in 2013, with the commonest species ringed being blue tit (1,097), siskin (752), great tit (567), swallow (259) and willow warbler (145).

Comparing the Central region to Britain and Ireland ringing totals, of particular significance were the ringed totals for red kite (84/486=17 %), buzzard (70/560=12 %), raven (39/329=12 %), osprey (21/203=10 %) and tawny owl (55/787=7 %).

Other notable species ringed in the region in 2013 include sparrowhawk (13), kestrel (18), peregrine (9), jack snipe (10), woodcock (26), barn owl (46), spotted flycatcher (4), pied flycatcher (74), redstart (18) and tree sparrow (44).

Notable ringing recoveries during 2013 are as follows.

WHOOPER SWAN *Cygnus cygnus*

A female, ringed as a nestling in Stawy Ozarow, Mokrsko, Poland on 5 Aug 2010, was seen on 26 Jun 2013 at L Katrine (identified by its neck collar). It was seen again a few days later (29 Jun 2013) at L Oire, Elgin. This was in any case an unusual June record of this species for the region and of additional interest because of its birthplace in Poland. Whooper swans began breeding in Poland in 1973 and numbers had grown to around 25 pairs by 2008. We tend to think of 'our' Whooper Swans as coming from the north/north-east – not so in this case.

RED KITE *Milvus milvus*

Most Upper Forth birders will be familiar with the red kite reintroduction project in the region, and with the Argaty feeding station. A young male seen here on 19 Jan 2013 had been ringed as a nestling (and wing-tagged) 6 months earlier in Dingwall, Highland – 159 km away. A short distance from Argaty, at Straid near Callander, two tagged birds were observed on 10 Jan 2013. Amazingly, both were immigrants from Highland - the first had been ringed as a nestling male on 17 Jun 2011 at the Heights of Docharty, Dingwall (157 km away, observed at 1 y 6 m 24 d old) and the other was also a male ringed as a nestling, this time at Easter Culbo, Black Isle (156 km away, observed at 0 y 6 m 29 d old). Finally, one of 'our' birds, ringed and tagged near Argaty on 24 Jun 2010, was recovered freshly dead near Aboyne, Grampian (125 km away, found at 2 y 9 m 14 d old).

BUZZARD *Buteo buteo*

There are two contrasting records of this species worth highlighting. Firstly, a bird ringed as a nestling on 23 Jun 2005 in Doune was recovered freshly dead on 06 Apr 2013 in the Cromlix Estate near Kinbuck, just 8 km from where it had been ringed. At 7 y 9 m 14 d old it was among the oldest ringing recoveries of this species in 2013. Note that the longevity record for Buzzard was set in 2013, with a freshly dead adult recovered on 27 Jul 2013 in Cumbria, ringed as a nestling in 1985 just 12 km away (28 y 1 m 11 d). By contrast, a nestling ringed in Doune on 27 Jun 2013 was found killed by a car on 15 Nov 2013 at Rossie Braes, Montrose – 111 km away (0 y 4 m 19 d). This was one of the longest recorded Buzzard movements within Britain & Ireland in 2013.

OSPREY *Pandion haliaetus*

A bird ringed as a nestling near Killin on 28 Jun 2008 has been seen alive on a few occasions, identified by its colour-rings. Previous sightings were on 25 May 2010 at Balgavies Loch, Tayside and 14 Apr 2011 at Upper Dicker, Sussex. This year, on 25 Mar 2013, the bird was found sick at Worton Fishery, Devizes, Wiltshire (aged 4 y 8 m 25 d).

KESTREL *Falco tinnunculus*

A nestling ringed on 20 Jun 2013 near Argaty, Stirling, was found just 1 month and 16 days later a staggering 181 km away at Findochty, near Elgin (Grampian). Sadly the youngster was dead. A short but eventful life...

CHIFFCHAFF *Phylloscopus collybita*

A juvenile ringed in Lionthorn Community Woods, Falkirk, on 09-09-2012 was caught by a ringer ~6 months later on 02 Mar 2013 at Gwennap Sewage Works, Cornwall. At 647 km this was the longest recorded movement by this species in 2013. Given the early-March recovery date it seems likely that this bird overwintered in the UK.

SEDGE WARBLER *Acrocephalus schoenobaenus*

An adult ringed at Blairdrummond on 30 May 2013 was caught by a ringer ~3 months later on 23 Aug 2013 at Etang-De-Moisan, Messanges, SW France – 1,386 km away. This was the only overseas recovery during 2013 of any Sedge Warblers which had been ringed in Britain and Ireland.

MEADOW PIPIT *Anthus pratensis*

A first year bird ringed at Spurn Head on 13 Sep 2012 was found freshly killed by a cat on 29 Jun 2013 near Fintry. This movement, of 388 km, was one of only two >100 km movements by this species recorded in 2013 in Britain and Ireland.

CHAFFINCH *Fringilla coelebs*

It notable that all three of the >100 km movements of this species recorded in 2013 involved the Central Region. An adult male ringed on 12 Apr 2012 in Balnain, Highland, was found freshly killed by a cat on 16 Feb 2013 in Killearn (149 km). An adult male ringed on 28 Dec 2010 in Aberfoyle Forest was caught by ringer on 28 Jan 2012 in Leswalt, Dumfries & Galloway (144 km). Finally a juvenile male ringed on 22 Aug 2006 in Peebles, Borders, was found freshly dead on 09 Jun 2013 at Inverherive, near Crianlarich (124 km). This latter bird was also one of the oldest Chaffinches recovered in 2013, aged 6 y 9 m 18 d. The longevity record for this species is 12 years 12 days.

SISKIN *Carduelis spinus*

This species provided quite a few interesting records in 2013. Firstly, birds that were ringed in the region. A second-year female ringed on 26 May 2013 in Callander was found dead on 09 Dec 2013 in Elstead, Surrey (609 km). A full-grown male ringed on 16 Mar 2012 in Aberfoyle Forest was caught by a ringer on 05 Feb 2013 in Chilworth, Surrey (606 km). Amazingly, a full-grown female ringed on the same day in Aberfoyle Forest (16 Mar 2012) was also caught by a ringer in Surrey in February (26 Feb 2013 at Molesey Lock, 592 km away). That three birds have been recorded making more-or-less the same movement, from ~Callander to Surrey, is remarkable.

There were also two recorded movements in the other direction, from the home counties up to the Central Region. An adult ringed on 10 Oct 2011 at Aldermaston Gravel Pit in Berkshire was caught by a ringer on 14 May 2013 in Callander (576 km). A first-year female ringed on 17 Mar 2013 in Chiddingstone, Kent was caught by a ringer just ~2 months later on 25 May 2013 in Callander (629 km).

Two birds which had been ringed overseas were also recovered in the Central Region in 2013. A full-grown male ringed on 20 Mar 2013 in Zand, Antwerpen, Belgium and a first-year female ringed on 4 Apr 2012 in Hockai, Liege, Belgium were both caught by a ringer in Callander on 11 May 2013 and 05 May 2013 respectively (having travelled 797 km and 930 km respectively). The male had made its ~800 km journey in around 7 weeks.

LESSER REDPOLL *Carduelis cabaret*

There were only four long distance (>100 km) recoveries of this species in Britain and Ireland in 2013 and all involved the Central Region. An adult male was ringed in 10 Oct 2012 at Pett Level, Sussex and was caught by a ringer on 11 May 2013 in Callander (675 km). A first-year female was ringed on 13 Oct 2012 in Kessingland, Suffolk and was caught by a ringer on 14 May 2013 in Callander (574 km). A full-grown male was ringed on 15 Apr 2012 at Timble Ings in North Yorkshire and was found dead on 23 May 2013 in Lochearnhead (313 km). Finally, a full-grown female was ringed on 07 Feb 2013 in Penrith, Cumbria and was caught by a ringer on 11 May 2013 in Callander (197 km).

BULLFINCH *Pyrrhula pyrrhula*

The longest recorded movement of the year within Britain & Ireland was a first-year female that had been ringed in Thetford, Norfolk (home to BTO's UK headquarters) and was recovered freshly dead on 11 Jan 2013 in Bridge of Allan (home of BTO's Scottish headquarters). A distance of 517 km.

GET INVOLVED

If reading about these fascinating ringing discoveries has inspired you to find out more, or to get involved, visit http://www.bto.org/volunteer-surveys/ringing/ringing-scheme

Report of the *Forth Naturalist and Historian* Wildlife and Landscape Forum, Saturday 7 September 2013

The *Forth Naturalist & Historian* held its third *Wildlife and Landscape Forum* at the Larbert High School. The first Forum, in 2011, aimed to bring together and showcase the huge range of activities being undertaken by so many societies and community groups in the Forth Valley. The 2013 Forum has followed a similar format to its predecessors – a mixture of longer and shorter talks and a wide variety of stalls. The Board of the *Forth Naturalist and Historian* is very grateful to Falkirk Council for providing funds to support the 2013 Forum and to Guy Harewood for his efforts in organising the third Forum in a row.

People were welcomed to the meeting by FNH's chairman, Michael Usher. He introduced Joan Peterson, the Deputy Leader of Falkirk Council. She welcomed people to the Falkirk District, and foresaw the possibility of much synergy between local groups in Falkirk and the FNH.

Roy Sexton began the series of talks by referring to the journal of the *Forth Naturalist and Historian*. He explained that in 1974 the British Association for the Advancement of Science's annual meeting (now called the British Science Festival) was held at the relatively new University of Stirling. For this visit a survey of the Central Region was undertaken – this included reviews of climate, geology, vegetation, mammals, fish, birds, settlements and the local economy. It was apparent to the authors that because the publication of the *Transactions of the Stirling Natural and Archaeological Society* (1878-1939) had ceased, there had subsequently been relatively little local study and an attempt was initiated to revive it. Academics from the University and staff from Central Regional Council got together with the objective of publishing a journal and running a conference annually to encourage the local study of both natural and social history. Central Region, which has now been split into Stirling, Falkirk and Clackmannan, was to provide the focus. Now 347 articles have now been published in *FNH*'s journal, the 36th volume is soon to be published and the 38th conference to be held.

Many of the earlier articles in the journal were general in nature and covered the whole Forth Region. The first five volumes had accounts of the climate, geomorphology, the woodlands, the fish, the ecology of the Forth, etc. These provided the local background for the new environmental science courses at the University and the increased emphasis on local studies in the fifth and sixth years at school. The recent trend has been for more specific local articles, such as the accounts of both plants and butterflies of Falkirk. In recent issues authors have also dealt with two of Falkirk's rareties, the orchid on Almond Bing known as Young's Helleborine (now *Epipactis helleborine* var. *youngiana*) and the Bean Goose (*Anser* fabalis) which overwinters on the

Slamannan Plateau. In addition the journal has provided a home for the annual records of local ornithologists, botanists and entomologists. The annual bird report is particularly rich in information about wader and water fowl records from the internationally important roosting sites at Skinflats and Kinneil.

Angus Smith, the Reserves Coordinator for Falkirk Members' Centre of the Scottish Wildlife Trust (SWT), talked about the Trust's five reserves in the Falkirk Local Authority area. Bo'mains Meadows has recently become a Coronation Meadow, within a scheme to create sixty such meadows throughout the United Kingdom to commemorate the 60th anniversary of the Coronation of the Queen. Until 1990 the reserve (2.68 ha) was the Bo'ness Town water supply reservoir, which was then drained and bulldozed more or less level. The north meadow has only received light grazing since 1884 and is now a Site of Special Scientific Interest (SSSI). The south meadow has an abundance of orchid species, including greater butterfly, common spotted and northern marsh orchids and common twayblade. Carron Dam was originally the water supply for the Carron Ironworks. The open water was maintained by the feeding of a large flock of mute swans until after the ironworks closed in 1974. This has now reverted to fenland, unique in the Falkirk area, with only a small area of open water, and is a SSSI. The area became a Local Nature Reserve in 2012. A local Community Group and SWT, together with Larbert High School, are involved in its management. Carron Glen, the SWT's 100th reserve, includes semi ancient woodland with associated plants, the most notable of which is globeflower. Water birds frequenting the reserve include dipper, heron and gooseander.

Wallacebank Wood contains 16 ha of semi-natural deciduous woodland, with oak of fairly even age. The wood had become badly infested by rhododendron, which was probably planted as cover for pheasants; members of the Falkirk group worked over a period of 25 years before finally clearing this invasive species. The wood hosts a good variety of woodland plants and mammals. Jupiter Urban Wildlife Centre is situated in a former industrial estate in Grangemouth and was officially opened in the spring of 1992. The bulk of the area, originally railway sidings consisting of hard packed ash, was landscaped and developed as an educational facility for use by local people and schools.

Dan Jackman, the chair of the steering group that organised Nature-Fest, Falkirk area's wildlife festival, explained how an idea was hatched in a pub! It was tested at FNH's 2012 *Wildlife and Landscape Forum* in Alloa, leading to a meeting with nineteen organisations or local groups in December 2012. Following this, a steering group was appointed to arrange a festival, including forming a partnership with the Forth Naturalist and Historian. The steering group obtained funding from Falkirk Council and Falkirk Environment Trust. A programme of 44 events between 18 May and 30 June 2013 was put together. Five thousand A3 brochures were designed, printed and distributed. A website was created and designed to match the brochure. A launch event was held in April 2013 at the Falkirk Wheel.

The average attendance at events was about ten, although some were particularly poorly attended. The most popular event was the 'Go Wild in the Glen', organised by the Westquarter Wildlife Group. About 300 people visited Westquarter Glen and Westquarter Primary School to see stalls, presentations, activities and, in the evening, a guided bat walk. Those who did attend gave very positive feedback and said they had learnt something. Thus, overall the festival had achieved its aims, but clearly for 2014 there should be more of a focus on maximising attendances.

Lorna Blackmore spoke about a project which she had undertaken at the University of Stirling. Insect pollinators play a crucial role in terrestrial ecosystems with more than half of all flowering plants depending on them for the successful pollination. This has huge ecological consequences for the organisms that depend on these plants; including humans for the ecosystem services they provide (e.g. in agriculture and horticulture). However, many of these beneficial insects have suffered declines in recent decades, largely due to the loss of suitable forage habitat. Methods such as establishing wildflower plots have been implemented to try and remedy this, particularly for bumblebees.

The project aimed to assess the effectiveness of the wildflower seed mix used by the local voluntary group, 'On the Verge'. The wildflower plots were surveyed to establish how many bumblebee species were visiting them, their abundance and what plant species they were feeding from. Different species of bumblebee have different tongue lengths which dictate which flowers they can feed from. A range of wildflowers is therefore needed to cater to all of these species; bumblebees require a range of flowers so as to maintain a healthy population with a diet of different types of pollen and nectar. Five species of bumblebee were recorded: buff-tailed, garden, red-tailed and white-tailed bumblebees and common carder bee. It was found that perennial/biennial wildflowers supported greater species diversity and abundance of bumblebees and that those plants in the pea family, such as red clover, were by far the most frequently visited flowers. Wild flowers often support more bumblebees than horticultural varieties – see *www.bumblebeeconservation.org* for advice of what to plant in a garden.

Alison Baker of the River Forth Fisheries Trust spoke about the work being undertaken by the Trust as part of its Forth Invasive Non Native Species programme (FINNS). This has attracted a number of funders including LEADER, Stirling Council, Falkirk Environmental Trust and Loch Lomond and Trossachs National Park. The scheme is a strategic and community based programme to tackle invasive species along the riparian corridor of the Forth District rivers. Invasive non native species can cause a number of problems, including monoculture (biodiversity loss), bank erosion, access issues, flooding and predation. The programme is concentrating on six main species – giant hogweed, Japanese knotweed, Himalayan balsam, skunk cabbage, American mink and signal crayfish – and is working on all the main river systems within the Forth District.

The programme aims to collect data across the District so as to identify the source and location of invasive species, and hence that a strategy can be put in place in each catchment to treat, control and monitor the species. It has been identified that rivers are good pathways for the distribution of the species; in aiming to eliminate the species from the corridor, treatment work must be from the top of the catchment down. To aid in the collection of data, a map-based reporting website has been developed in conjunction with River and Fisheries Trusts of Scotland. Whilst some work is being undertaken by contractors, the scheme is training and equipping volunteers from local groups and communities to be able to undertake the management work. FINNS aims to help local groups tackle the problems caused by these species and then monitor the environment in a sustainable manner.

Joanna Girvan, biologist to the Forth River Fisheries Trust, presented an Award for an outstanding volunteer contribution for restoration of the water environment to George Mackintosh, Slamannan Angling and Protective Association.

Michael Usher gave a brief resumé of the FNH's activities, from its long series of annual conferences and journal volumes, to the first *Wildlife and Landscape Forum* in 2011, its launch as a membership society and the introduction of a lecture and AGM in 2012, and the launch of a *Historical and Archaeological Forum* in 2013. He posed a number of questions about the content of the journal, about themes for future conferences, and about the Forums being even more inclusive. The board of FNH wish to see this as a vibrant Society, being of service to everyone in the Council Districts of Clackmannanshire, Falkirk and Stirling. He ended by looking forward to the 2013 FNH conference, to be held on 16 November on the *Changing Biodiversity of Central Scotland*. This is reported on elsewhere in this journal.

There were short talks by Walter Atwood (Friends of the Earth Stirling) on the threat from unconventional energy, by Christine Bell and Vivien Murchison on exploring our rivers, by David Payne on the proposed *Forth Wildlife Forum*, and by Peter Paterson of the Save Gillies Hill campaign. Stalls and displays were provided by Butterfly Conservation Scotland, Buglife Scotland, CentARG (Central Amphibian and Reptile Group), Central Scotland Forest Trust, Communities Along the Carron, Falkirk Invasives Group, Falkirk LBAP, Falkirk Nature-Fest, Forth Environment Link and 'On the Verge', Forth Naturalist and Historian, Friends of Plean Country Park, Friends of the Earth Stirling, Ochils Landscape Partnership, River Forth Fisheries Trust, RSPB Futurescapes and Inner Forth Landscape Initiative, Save Gillies Hill Group, Scottish Wildlife Trust – Falkirk Members Group, Slamannan Angling and

Protective Association, Scottish Waterways Trust , SRUC – Oatridge Campus, Stirling Council Ranger Service, Stirling University Nature Society, and Westquarter Wildlife Group.

Michael B Usher

Plate 1a. Beautiful Snout (*Hypena crassalis*) Loch Ard David Smith

Plate 1b. *Palpita vitrealis* Bridge of Allan David Bryant

Plate 2. Central Region roadside boundary sign at Croftamie near Drymen.

Plate 3.

Crest of Clan Colquhoun. The encircling strap and buckle is a token of allegiance by clan members to their Chief.

Crest on the memorial stone to the 6th Duke of Montrose, Chief of Clan Graham.

Crests of two clans feature on the regimental badge of the Argyll and Sutherland Highlanders.

Plate 4. The 'Herd's Hoose' was situated in King's Park near what is now the golf course's 3rd green. It was painted by L. Baker in about 1860 (Courtesy Stirling Smith Art Gallery and Museum). The meadowland was famous for its displays of wild pansies (below) the last of which was recorded in 2007.

Plate 5. A few of the plants lost from King's Park. Bloody crane's-bill (top left) early purple orchid (top right) yellow star of Bethlehem (below).

Plate 6. Rookery at Union Canal, Hallglen, Falkirk.

Plate 7a. Slender brindle (*Apamea scolopacina*), a recent colonist of the Falkirk area (R. Young).

Plate 7b. Lempke's gold spot (*Plusia putnami*), previously a cryptic species of gold spot (*Plusia festucae*), first described in 1966 (R. Young).

Plate 8a. Female small china-mark (*Cataclysta lemnata*) egg-laying on duckweed; the male has pure white forewings (R. Young).

Plate 8b. Larva and larval case of small china-mark (*Cataclysta lemnata*) (H. Young).

Plate 9a

Plate 9b

Six species of hoverflies new to NS89 and NS90 were identified during the survey. These included:

Plate 9a: Female Twin-banded wasp-hoverfly (*Chrysotoxum bimaculatum*) © Steven Falk

Plate 9b: Female Copper sap-run hoverfly (*Ferdinandea cuprea*) © Steven Falk

Plate 10a. Head of the upper Carron Valley. Today the site of the former water-meadow is almost entirely covered over by a modern reservoir.

Plate 10b. Carron Bridge pastures – a last opportunity for the beasts to regain condition before going on show at the Falkirk Tryst.

Plate 11a. Large Heath Coenonympha tullia (polydama sub spp.) found on Butterfly Conservation's reserve at Wester Moss, Fallin. Photographed by Lorna Blackmore

Plate 11b. Purple Hairstreak (Female) Favonius quercus found on pedunculate oak near Kippenrait Glen. Photographed by Lorna Blackmore.

Plate 12a. Northern Brown Argus Aricia Artaxerxes photographed by Heather Young in Alva Glen.

Plate 12b. Northern Brown Argus egg on common rock-rose on Craig Leith. Inset: egg magnified. Photographed by Melissa Shaw.

THE UPPER CARRON VALLEY AND THE HIGHLAND DROVERS

John Mitchell

Until the second half of the 18th century, Stirlingshire's upper Carron Valley as a cross-country route was probably used by few travellers other than local people and the occasional visiting chapman or pedlar on his rounds of the scattered homesteads and farms. Change came about when Scotland's most important livestock fair for West Highland cattle or 'kyloes' – traditionally held at Crieff in Perthshire – began to decline in favour of an up and coming fair near Falkirk some twenty-six miles to the south. The County of Stirling had previously played no part in the movement of huge numbers of the small black 'kyloes' (Figure 1) as they made their way from the Highlands and Islands to the Crieff Tryst, but now as the cattle drovers sought out the quieter by-ways to reach Falkirk, a good many turned to the Carron Valley as their preferred choice.

Heading for the the Carron Valley

Following a period of dry weather and low water levels, drovers from the North and Central Highlands heading for the Carron Valley were able to cross the River Forth with their beasts at the Fords of Frew below Kippen. Advantageously, this side-stepped the custom dues demanded for the animals to cross the Forth at Stirling Bridge (Anon, 1755), together with additional costs if they could not avoid roads upgraded to pay-as-you-go turnpikes as they approached or departed the town (Gordon, 1988).

The Fords of Frew safely negotiated, the droves were then taken over the Fintry Hills from the Spout of Ballochleam to Burnfoot in the Endrick Valley (RCAHMS, 1963). Soft going underfoot for this part of the drive, the beasts benefited too from being able to snatch sustaining mouthfuls of herbage all along the way. Had the drovers no other option but to circumnavigate the high ground, by following the Kippen to Campsie Turnpike to reach the Endrick Valley meant a begrudged one penny to be paid for every head of cattle at either the Lernock or Fintry Tolls. Of further concern to the drovers would have been the wear and tear on the animals' hooves from the road surface made-up of broken stone, yet to allow the beasts to find easier walking on the turnpike's grass verges risked a fine of up to fifteen shillings (Anon, 1798).

From the Western Highlands and Islands, three distinct streams of cattle destined for Falkirk via the Carron Valley passed through Gartmore, Rowardennan (after the droves had been swum across Loch Lomond at its narrowest point) and Bonhill in the Vale of Leven (Mitchell, 2000). Continuing eastwards towards the head of Strathendrick, the drovers gave roads a miss wherever they could by taking to the open moorland. Along with the droves coming from the north over the Fintry Hills, all now crossed the Endrick watershed into the upper Carron Valley.

On to Carron Bridge

From the summit of the Endrick watershed, the drovers had their first glimpse of the famous Carron Meadow (Plate 10a), at 500 Scots acres (255 hectares) occupying almost all of the upper Carron Valley floor and reputed to be the largest water-meadow in the whole of Scotland (Mitchell, 2002). Even if the valuable hay it produced had already been cut and gathered in, the droves would still not have been permitted to cross the meadow for fear of the cattle trampling the carefully graded water channels laid out to irrigate the ground. Instead they deflected around the meadow to either the north or south.

A.R.B. Haldane in the accompanying map to his classic work *The Drove Roads of Scotland* (1952) suggests the drovers followed the Fintry to Denny road which ran alongside the meadow's northern edge. However, what was originally a free to use parish road seems likely to have been given a wide berth after it was turnpiked for at least half of its length (OS Name Book, 1858-1861). A Bonnybridge minister and local historian – the Reverend Thomas Miller (1869-1942) who researched and published a paper on the Falkirk Tryst (Miller, 1936) – describes the drovers taking the toll-free and soft underfoot alternative on the south side of the meadow. He recalled a gate inserted in the march dyke between the farms of Binns and Slachristock to allow the cattle to pass through as they made their way to Carron Bridge.

In a rapidly changing countryside where the Highland drovers were finding their freedom of movement increasingly restricted and the customary resting places or stances for the animals denied to them by the many new enclosures, Carron Bridge (Plate 10b) was one place which could be depended upon for an overnight or longer stay. In contrast to the poor reception the drovers often received elsewhere, it is apparent that Carron Bridge farmers looked upon the passage of drove after drove of travel-weary beasts as a business opportunity, for a consideration being prepared to offer them a much needed stance together with fresh grazing or good quality hay (Cregeen, 1959; Harrison, 2005). A welcome too could be expected from the Carron Bridge Inn, the innkeeper well used to catering for the drovers' needs. With the beasts rested, fed and watered, they would be driven the last few miles to Falkirk in time for the opening day of the sales.

Decline of the Droving Trade

The beginning of the end for the droving trade came with the spread of railways into the Scottish Highlands. This is tellingly reflected in an article that appeared in the *Stirling Observer* for 11 September 1856 … *Cattle for Falkirk Tryst: Although large numbers of cattle have passed through Stirling during the past week, from the north for Falkirk Tryst, still they have not been so numerous as in former years.*

Indeed we are informed, on the authority of the tacksman of customs at Stirling Bridge, that about 2000 head less of cattle have passed through Stirling this week than any former year of his experience. The fact is that many purchasers now proceed to the pasture grounds in the north and buy up large quantities of cattle at a cheaper rate than if they were brought to market. Abundant evidence of this may be had in the sometimes heavy trains which pass our station southwards, laden with vast numbers of cattle. From this it may be inferred that the tryst at Falkirk must have declined considerably in the number of beasts brought to market.

Market reports in newspapers of the time confirm that attendance at the Falkirk livestock sales continued to dwindle throughout the second half of the 19th century, the final gathering held at Stenhousemuir in 1901 (Cregeen, 1959). The Highland drovers with the 'kyloes' entrusted to them had made their way through the upper Carron Valley on the long trek to the Falkirk Tryst for the very last time.

Acknowledgement

My thanks to Peter Smith of the Drymen and District Local History Society for preparing my illustrations for publication.

References

Anon, 1755. *Table of the Customs of the Burgh of Stirling to be exacted at the Bridge and the Burgh Gate.* Stirling Council Archives, SB1/11/6/6.

Anon. 1798. *An Act for more effectively repairing several roads in the Counties of Stirling, Dumbarton and Perth.* Stirling Council Archives, SC2/9/3.

Cregeen, E. 1959. Recollections of an Argyllshire Drover. *Scottish Studies* **3**, 143-162.

Gordon, A. 1988. Turnpike Roads in *To Move with the Times: the Story of Transport and Travel in Scotland.* Aberdeen: University Press.

Harrison, J.G. 2005. Improving the Roads and Bridges in the Stirling Area c.1660-1706. *Proceedings of the Society of Antiquaries of Scotland* **135**, 287-307.

Miller, Rev. T. 1936. The Origin of the Falkirk Trysts. *Proceedings of the Falkirk Archaeological and Natural History Society* **1**, 25-47.

Mitchell, J. 2000. *The Shielings and Drove Ways of Loch Lomondside.* Stirling: Jamieson & Munro.

Mitchell, J. 2002. A former water-meadow in the Upper Carron Valley, Stirlingshire. *The Glasgow Naturalist* **24**, 59-63.

Ordnance Survey Name book, 1858-1861. Randieford Bridge in *Stirlingshire Vol. 13,* Parish of Fintry OS1/32/13/50. Edinburgh: National Records of Scotland.

Royal Commission on the Ancient and Historical Monuments of Scotland. 1963. Old Roads and Trysts in *Stirlingshire: An Inventory of the Ancient Monuments Vol. 2.* Edinburgh: HMSO.

Figure 1. Sharing a common ancestry, young Highland cattle bear a close resemblance to the hardy 'kyloes' which were once taken in their thousands to the Crieff and Falkirk Trysts.

LOCH LOMONDSIDE'S HERALDIC BIRDS AND BEASTS

John Mitchell

Introduction

In the eight hundred year old or so history of the pictorial language of heraldry in Scotland, it is evident that many of the birds and beasts which featured on the nobility's coats of arms were chosen because of characteristics most admired – the proud bearing of the stag, the dashing speed of the falcon, the strength of the lion. Ferocious creatures such the lion as a significant part of the arms could also reflect the holders' valour on the field of battle (Slater, 2004). Times may have changed, but the same or similar birds and beasts continue still to appear on present day coats of arms as well as the insignias of the armed services.

The author's curiosity about these symbolic animals was first aroused by the former Central Region's coat of arms, conspicuously displayed on roadside boundary signs following local government re-organisation throughout Scotland in 1975 (Plate 2.). The stories behind the heraldic bird and beast representing Central Region, together with other examples from the Loch Lomond area, are discussed and illustrated.

Central Region and Stirling Council

Supporting the Central Region's coat of arms was a goshawk and a unicorn. Birds of prey in heraldry as often as not have their roots in the ancient sport of hunting with hawks, a pursuit initially confined to persons of high standing. In this particular case, the goshawk recalls the armorial crest of the Drummonds (Urquhart, 1979; Dewar, 2001). An immigrant family first recorded in the 11th century as having settled at Drumyn (Drymen) – from where they took their name – descendants of these early Drummonds went on to acquire extensive land holdings in southern Perthshire. It was a James Drummond who in 1739 first visualised the planned town of Callander, an important 'gateway' to the Highlands within the region. Unfortunately, Drummond found himself on the losing side during the Jacobite Uprising of 1745/46, so that it fell to the Commissioners for the Forfeited Estates to carry through his far-sighted scheme. Why a mythical animal such as the unicorn was raised to such a high state in the heraldry of Scottish Kingship is less clear, but since 1603 when James VI of Scotland became James I of England as well, the unicorn has represented the House of Stuart in the Royal Arms of Great Britain (Brooke-Little, 1987).

After the dissolution of Central Region in 1996 and the emergence of its successor Stirling Council, the goshawk was again chosen as a supporter to the new coat of arms, but the unicorn lost its place to a wolf. This looks back to the once indigenous animal's role in the arms of the old Burgh of Stirling (Urquhart, 1973). How in the 9th century the alarm cries of a wolf gave the Stirling town guard a timely warning to the approach of Danish raiders, is well entrenched in local folklore.

Figure 1. Arms of the Lumsdens of Arden.

The Lumsdens of Arden

The wolf was to turn up again when the author was researching the life of the Loch Lomondside naturalist James Lumsden (1851-1911), eldest son of Sir James Lumsden of Arden – a former Lord Provost of the City of Glasgow (Burke, 1914; Lumsden, 1995). Anecdotal evidence suggests a link between the two wolves' heads on Sir James' coat of arms (Figure 1.) and a 13th century ancestor known as 'Old Wolf' who came from Lumsdaine in Berwickshire.

The Colquhouns of Luss

Just to the north of Arden House lies Rossdhu Park, the ruined castle there the ancestral seat of the Chief of Clan Colquhoun. Travellers from the south making their way to Luss up the main Loch Lomond road cannot fail to notice the impressive ornamental gates to the south entrance of the park. Above the archway is the Colquhoun coat of arms, its crest a red deer stag's head (Plate 3.).

The legend behind the stag's head as the Colquhoun clan crest can be dated to 1424 and the return to Scotland of James I after being held captive in England for many years. Engaged in re-establishing sovereign power over a divided country, King James turned to the staunchly loyal Sir John Colquhoun to wrest possession of Dumbarton Castle from rebel hands. It is said that Sir John's ingenious plan of action was to stage a hunt of a released stag close to the castle, successfully enticing the guards to leave their posts to watch or join in the chase. At this, Colquhoun's armed clansmen emerged from their hiding place, rushed the unattended entrance and gained control of the castle (MacPhail, 1979). A good story, but it ignores the fact that in the 15th century Dumbarton Castle was surrounded by tidal mudflats. Furthermore, any remnants of forest cover in the neighbourhood where the Colquhoun force might have lain concealed, had long before vanished in the face of timber requirements by both castle and town.

The Grahams of Mugdock

On the east side of Loch Lomond a noble family in its ascendency during the 17th century was the Grahams of Mugdock, in 1682 extending their land holding in the district by purchasing the Laird of Buchanan's estate (Eyre-Todd, 1915). In another example of a connection between heraldry and the practice of falconry, the crest of Clan Graham as usually depicted is an eagle standing over a heron (Plate 3.). Artistic licence would appear to have crept in at some time in the past, for when flying at herons the falconer's bird of choice would almost certainly have been a peregrine. Heron-hawking stood pre-eminent as a field sport amongst falconry enthusiasts, the hunting bird specifically trained to force its quarry down to the ground yet unharmed. Unlike game birds intended for the pot, the practically inedible heron would be released back into the wild.

The Argyll and Sutherland Highlanders

With battalions having been raised at both Stirling and Dumbarton, this famous Scottish regiment has a close association with the general area. Formed in 1881 by an amalgamation of the 91st (Argyllshire) Highlanders and the 93rd (Sutherland) Highlanders, the new regiment took the name Princess Louise's Argyll and Sutherland Highlanders, adopting its predecessors' insignias of Clan Campbell's crest of a wild boar's head and Clan Sutherland's crest of a Scottish wild cat with claws unsheathed (Asquith, 1998).

The wild cat as an armorial device is known from the earliest days of Scottish heraldry (Kilshaw, 2011), with several clans having adopted the 'Highland Tiger' as their crest or badge. Clan Campbell's choice of a boar's head as its crest can be traced back to the reign of James II (1437-1460). The tale as passed down tells of a son of Sir Duncan Campbell of Loch Awe being granted extensive lands in Argyll by King James, a reward for slaying a notorious wild boar which had been terrorising the Loch Lomondside inhabitants (Wallace, 1899).

As part of the restructuring of the British Army which took place in 2006, the Argyll and Sutherland Highlanders ceased to be an independent unit when they were absorbed into the Royal Regiment of Scotland. The wild cat and wild boar clan crests (Plate 3.) can still be seen however on the Argylls' cap badge and other uniform accoutrements displayed in the regimental museum housed at Stirling Castle.

Acknowledgements

I am grateful to Phil Graham and Archie Lumsden for generously making available information on their respective forebears. Thanks are also due to Rod MacKenzie of the Argyll and Sutherland Highlanders Museum, Stirling, for verifying aspects of the regiment's insignia. The illustrations accompanying this article were prepared for publication by Peter Smith of the Drymen and District Local History Society.

References

Asquith, S. (ed.). 1998. The Argyll and Sutherland Highlanders 1794-1881. *Regiment* No. 31.

Brooke-Little, J.P. 1987. *Royal Heraldry: Beasts and Badges of Britain.* Derby: Pilgrim Press.

Burke, Sir B. 1914. *Landed Gentry of Great Britain (12th edn.).* London: Harrison & Sons).

Dewar, P.B. (ed.). 2001. *Burke's Landed Gentry of Great Britain: The Kingdom in Scotland (19th edn.).* London: Fitzroy Dearborn.

Eyre-Todd, G. 1915. The Gallant Grahams and the House of Montrose. *Scottish Country Life.* **2**, 57-61.

Kilshaw, K. 2011. *Scottish Wildcats.* Batttleby: Scottish Natural Heritage.

Lumsden, A. 1995. *The Arms of Lumsden (2nd edn.).* Kilrenny: House of Lumsden Association.

MacPhail, I.M.M. 1979. *Dumbarton Castle.* Edinburgh: John Donald.

Slater, S. 2004. *The History and Meaning of Heraldry.* London: Anness publishing.

Urquhart, R.M. 1973. *Scottish Burgh and County Heraldry.* London: Heraldry Today.

Urquhart, R.M. 1979. *Scottish Civic Heraldry: Regional – Islands – District.* London: Heraldry Today.

Wallace, T.D. 1899. The Wild Boar in Britain. *Transactions of the Inverness Scientific Society and Field Club.* **5**, 296-305.

PREHISTORIC POTTERY FROM EXCAVATIONS AT THE SMITH ART GALLERY AND MUSEUM, STIRLING

Nick Aitchison

A trial excavation in the grounds of the Smith Art Gallery and Museum, Stirling, revealed possible archaeological features and yielded four sherds of prehistoric pottery, one from a Food Vessel urn of early Bronze Age date.

The Excavation

In November 1977, volunteers from the Stirling Field and Archaeological Society opened a trial trench in the grounds of the Smith Art Gallery and Museum (the 'Smith'), Dumbarton Road, Stirling (NS 791 936). The objective of the excavation was to evaluate the archaeological potential of the site in advance of a proposed development, although this never proceeded.

The site is of possible archaeological interest for several reasons:

- Its proximity to a multivallate earthwork enclosure of possibly prehistoric date beneath the King's Knot (NS 789 937).
- The possible proximity of the presumed, but so far undiscovered, Roman fort at or near Stirling. An enduring antiquarian tradition places this fort at, or beneath, the King's Knot (Maitland, 1757: 194; Crawford, 1949: 22).
- The potential survival of undisturbed archaeological deposits. The grounds have remained undeveloped since the construction of the 'Smith' in 1871-4 and its location at the foot of Stirling's Castle Rock suggested that deep deposits resulting from both human activity and natural processes, including the erosion of soil from the hillside, may have accumulated there. Such deposits might contain evidence of human activity and/or preserve archaeological remains beneath them.

The limited results obtained justified the decision to excavate but were never published, possibly because the significance of the sherds was not recognised at the time.

The excavation was conducted in the centre of an enclosed area behind the 'Smith'. Roughly triangular in plan, this area is defined by a line of mature trees on the south, the boundary walls with Greenwood Avenue on the north-east and the lane behind Royal Gardens on the west. This space is now occupied by Ailie's Garden, a biodiversity education and play area, but was unused and laid to grass in 1977. A trench orientated north-south and measuring approximately 10 m by 2 m was opened. Faint traces of this trench are still visible but no plans, sections or photographs of the excavation appear to have survived.

A considerable depth of golden brown loam, with no discernible stratigraphy, was encountered immediately beneath the topsoil. This layer appeared to be anthropogenic in origin, probably a cultivated or garden soil. This is consistent with the agricultural status of this area, which was part of the Rude Croft, before the 'Smith' was built (Aitken et al., 1984: 18-19). William Roy's map of 1747-55 depicts fields here, their rigs and furrows clearly shown. Several sherds of late medieval green glazed pottery belonging to a flagon or pitcher were found near the top of this layer. Many of these sherds joined, suggesting that the vessel was broken in situ. Regrettably, these sherds were later lost. Sherd 1 (below) was found at a greater depth within this deposit.

Three or four flat stones and a single possible stake hole were eventually encountered beneath this soil, at a depth of almost 2 m. These stones appeared to be of sandstone, in contrast to the naturally-occurring quartz-dolerite whinstone of Castle Rock. Although these stones superficially appeared to form rough paving, they were unworn and may have belonged to a natural feature, perhaps consistent with an early seashore. These stones rested on gravel, apparently a natural deposit, which was not further explored. There was no occupation deposit above the gravel or possible paving, although their surfaces were covered in a thin layer of probably naturally-occurring fine gravel. Three sherds of pottery, Sherds 2, 3 and 4 (below), were found in this fine gravel layer.

The Pottery

Four sherds of prehistoric pottery, belonging to three different vessels, were found. Two of these are rim sherds, the upper part of a vessel around its mouth. Rim sherds are important because they usually provide more stylistic information than body or wall sherds and allow the diameter of the mouth of the vessel to be estimated. The form, size, function and date of the vessel may be inferred from these characteristics. The other two fragments are body sherds, one of them from the same vessel as one of the rim sherds. The total weight of pottery is 40 g, giving an average weight for each sherd of 10 g. Each sherd was examined to produce a basic description of its fabric and stylistic attributes, including size, shape, colour, surface treatment, type of temper and residues. These properties have implications for the manufacture, use and date of the vessels represented.

Fabric analysis was undertaken only at a basic, macroscopic, level. Although convenient and inexpensive, this makes it difficult to identify grit inclusions. Any observations on these, therefore, are only provisional unless confirmed by microscopic analysis. Inclusions originate in the manufacture of the vessels. Crushed stone was often added to wet clay as temper to reduce plasticity, making it easier to work, and to reduce shrinkage or expansion during the firing process (Gibson and Woods, 1997: 213-15, 257-61).

Sherd 1

This body sherd (Figure 1) measures 42 mm by 23 mm and is 11 mm thick. Its curvature indicates that it belonged to a vessel measuring approximately 210 mm in diameter, although its height and rim diameter are unknown. The sherd has a coarse and reasonably hard clay fabric with frequent inclusions in its exterior surface, which is orange-buff in colour. Very fine, possibly micaceous, inclusions are visible in the fabric but may occur naturally within the clay. Inclusions are less noticeable in the interior because the fabric is black in colour and partly obscured by a deposit (below). Most inclusions are black or brown, angular to sub-angular and apparently of igneous rock, with a small number of white, apparently quartz, inclusions. The inclusions are moderately well sorted and up to 1 mm across.

This sherd displays evidence of both construction and use. The break on one side of the sherd is smooth and slopes at a 45 degree angle to the vessel wall. This may result from two adjacent building sections of clay not being bonded properly during manufacture, leaving a join void which increases in size as the clay shrinks during the drying process (see Gibson and Woods, 1997: 152, 194-5). Such voids create weaknesses and vessels tend to break along these, leaving rounded edges, formerly referred to as 'false rims'. In this case, the broken edge is sloping rather than rounded in profile, which is characteristic of construction using overlapping strips or slabs of clay. The orange-coloured exterior fabric reveals that this vessel was fired in an oxidising atmosphere, characterised by the presence of excess oxygen, resulting in total combustion. The oxidisation of iron oxides present in clay results in a red or reddish-brown colour, consistent with open firing in a pit or bonfire (Gibson and Woods, 1997: 49-54, 216).

A black encrustation adhering to the interior surface of Sherd 1 appears to be a carbonised deposit, presumably resulting from cooking foodstuffs over an open fire. This probably explains the black interior of the sherd, where organic deposits have been absorbed by the fabric. Scientific analysis may reveal the nature of this residue, which may also be suitable for radiocarbon dating.

Sherd 2

This rim sherd measures 36 mm long and up to 28 mm in depth of the profile is present (Figures 2 and 3). Its curvature reveals that the vessel had an external diameter of approximately 190 mm at its mouth, meaning that approximately 6 % of the rim circumference is present. The rim is everted, bevelled on the interior and is 7 mm wide at the point where the bevel returns to the wall. A single cordon, 9 mm wide, is located 12 mm below the rim. This cordon is not symmetrical but has a slightly sinuous profile. The wall thickness of the vessel is unclear because so little of the sherd survives below the cordon, but appears to be 4 or 5 mm. All surfaces are undecorated.

Sherd 2 has a relatively fine, hard clay fabric. The interior surface is predominantly greyish-white, with a light grey patch, while the exterior is a creamy white. The sherd is heavily gritted with inclusions of dark grey and brown angular to sub-angular igneous rock, many protruding from the interior and exterior surfaces. Its pitted surface reveals where other inclusions have become detached during firing, subsequent use or deposition. The inclusions are moderately well sorted and up to 1 mm across, except for a larger inclusion of igneous rock, 3 mm by 4 mm, on the outer edge of the rim. The exterior below the cordon has a better quality finish, with smaller and fewer inclusions, producing a smoother surface.

In handmade pottery, the junction between an everted and/or thickened rim and the body of the vessel is often where two rings or coils of clay have been joined, creating a weakness around the vessel wall (Gibson and Woods, 1997: 118). Sherd 2 has broken along such a line, just below the cordon. A slight groove around the lower edge of the cordon, where it meets the vessel wall, has been produced by running a finger nail or hard object around the wet clay vessel before firing.

The centre or core of the fabric is grey in colour and significantly darker than the surfaces, providing evidence of firing conditions. A darker core is produced when carbonaceous matter, finely divided organic material that occurs naturally in most clays, is not completely combusted during firing. Carbonaceous matter burns out at temperatures above 250 °C, although most effective combustion is achieved between 700 and 800 °C. A darker core reveals that the firing time was too short to achieve total combustion and is characteristic of open firing, in a bonfire or pit, without a kiln structure (Gibson and Woods, 1997: 118-19, 212-13). Sherd 2 shows no evidence of use, with no visible residues or abrasion relating to use on its surfaces.

Sherds 3 and 4

Sherd 3 is a rim sherd (Figures 4 and 5) and Sherd 4 is a body sherd (Figure 6). Although they do not join, these sherds share the same fabric, colour and wall thickness, revealing that they belong to the same vessel. This vessel had an external diameter of approximately 200 mm at its mouth. Approximately 5 % of the rim circumference and up to 16 mm in depth of the profile are present. The rim is very distinctive. It is both everted and expanded to form a thickened, angular lip, trapezoidal in profile, with distinct surfaces: an interior rim face, rim top and exterior rim face. There is also a pronounced internal shoulder carination. The wall is 3 mm thick where the lip joins the body of the vessel and the flat rim top is 8 mm wide. All surfaces are undecorated.

Sherd 4 measures up to 26 mm by 23 mm and has a band of either two small ridges, 6 mm wide, or three shallow grooves. These presumably continued horizontally around the vessel.

Sherds 3 and 4 have a fine, hard clay fabric with frequent inclusions protruding from both the interior and exterior surfaces. The interior surface is cream, while the exterior is predominantly light grey and the exterior of the rim is dark grey. Both sherds have inclusions of black or reddish-brown angular to sub-angular igneous rock. The inclusions are mostly well sorted and about 0.5 mm across, although one in the rim sherd measures 2 mm across. Sherd 3, like Sherd 2, has broken along a weakness between the rim and body. A fine groove defining the junction of the vessel rim and body on both the interior and exterior surfaces has been produced by running a finger nail or implement around the wet clay vessel before firing. Evidence of firing is visible in the cross-sections of Sherds 3 and 4. The core of the fabric is mid- or dark grey, resulting from a low firing temperature and short firing time, as with Sherd 2. These sherds display no evidence of use, with no visible residues or abrasion on the surfaces.

Stylistic Affinities

Sherd 1 lacks diagnostic features but shares several characteristics – fabric type and colour, wall thickness and the large size of the vessel it belongs to – with pottery found in the King's Park, Stirling (Aitchison, 2013), 850 m south-south-west of the excavation site. Sherd 1 probably belongs to a later prehistoric urn, dating sometime between *c.* 1700 BC and the early centuries AD.

Sherd 2 is more easily identified and closely dated. Its distinctive rim profile and darker core of its fabric are characteristic of Food Vessels. Food Vessel is a generic category, embracing a wide variety of vessel shapes, sizes and decoration. However, a broad distinction between bowl- and vase-shaped vessels is widely accepted (e.g. Gibson and Woods, 1997: 119, 158-65). Food Vessel urns, sometimes referred to as 'enlarged Food Vessel urns' or 'vase urns', are tall vessels with a height greater than their maximum diameter (Cowie, 1978: 20-4). Its rim diameter reveals that Sherd 2 belonged to a Food Vessel urn. Although some Food Vessels are plain, most are richly decorated with complex patterns of incised, impressed or applied decoration (Cowie, 1978: 24-8). Sherd 2 is now undecorated, but both its interior and exterior surfaces are rough, suggesting loss of surface detail to erosion.

Sherd 3 presents a greater challenge. The form of the vessel is uncertain. The angle between the rim and wall suggests that its mouth was narrower than its body, indicating that the vessel may have been barrel-shaped or globular in form. Such a distinctive rim morphology should facilitate diagnosis, both stylistic and chronological, although no direct parallels have been identified. Nevertheless, several diagnostic features may be identified. Vessels with elaborate rim forms, including angular, bevelled and moulded rims, were characteristic of several pottery traditions during the late Neolithic period in northern Britain, and it is from these that Food Vessels evolved. In particular, the rim moulding of late third and early second millennia BC pottery is usually angular and complements a bevel (Gibson and Woods, 1997: 118-19, 239). The elaborate nature of the rim suggests that the grooves or ridges on Sherd 4 belonged to the neck or upper body of the vessel. This is consistent with the tendency for the necks and bodies of late Neolithic and early Bronze Age pottery to be divided into zones with carination, collars, cordons or decoration. These features suggest that Sherds 3 and 4 belong to the late Neolithic or early Bronze Age (*c.* 3000-1700 BC). The combination of large vessel size, narrow wall thickness and elaborate rim attest the potter's skill, particularly given the simple firing conditions.

Discussion

Food Vessels are a distinctively early Bronze Age form of pottery. Their name, like that of Beakers, reflects an antiquarian interpretation of their function and their actual purpose is unclear. Although poorly dated until recently, increasingly reliable radiocarbon dating techniques now reveal that Food Vessels were in use around 2100 BC (Sheridan, 2003: 203-6; 2004).

The distribution of Food Vessels urns in Scotland is focused on the east (Sheridan, 2003: 205, fig. 13.3), where they usually accompany a crouched inhumation in a cist. This is also the case in the Stirling area. Although poorly recorded, six Food Vessels, some of them in cists, were found in the Birkhill and Coneypark areas (centred on NS 781 926) during the nineteenth century (RCAHMS, 1979: 7, no. 8, 10-11, nos 33-7, 42-3). This suggests that Sherd 2, and possibly Sherds 3 and 4, may have originated in an early Bronze Age burial. The absence of supporting evidence – in the form of human remains, a cist or traces of funerary monuments – may be attributable to the small scale of the excavation and/or to disturbance in antiquity. No Bronze Age burials are recorded in the vicinity of the 'Smith'. It has been suggested that the mound forming the centrepiece of the King's Knot may have reused an ancient burial monument (Cook, 1907: 132-3), although recent geophysical survey (Digney and Jones, 2013) does not support this. As early Bronze Age burial mounds usually occupy sites with a more open aspect, both the 'Smith' and the King's Knot, sited at the foot of Castle Rock, seem unlikely locations for funerary monuments of this period. However, the extensive and dramatic view to the north-west, across the Carse of Forth to the hills and the setting sun behind them, may have given this area a ritual significance during the early Bronze Age.

Alternatively, a presumption that the Food Vessel sherd originated in a burial may reflect a bias in archaeological preservation and discovery. Early Bronze Age burials, particularly those within or beneath funerary monuments or in cists, are more likely to survive and attract archaeological interest. By contrast, settlement sites of this period are notoriously elusive. Nevertheless, Food Vessels or sherds have been recovered from domestic sites in the Western Isles, at Dalmore (Lewis), Silgenach (South Uist), and Ardnave and Kilellan Farm (both Islay).

The discovery of a Food Vessel sherd and two late Neolithic or early Bronze Age sherds belonging to the same vessel in the same trench indicates that these are unlikely to be stray finds. Instead, these sherds were presumably derived from activity on, or within the immediate vicinity of, the site. However, there is little to indicate the nature and function of this activity. The pottery, possible paving and stake hole do not, by themselves, comprise evidence of a settlement but may be suggestive of one. A concentration of early Bronze Age burials in the area between Cambusbarron and the King's Park attests the presence of a thriving community or communities to the south-west of Stirling, but the nature and location(s) of their settlement(s) are unknown. The 'Smith' lies only 1.3 km to the north-east and occupies an attractive settlement site, south-facing and sheltered in the lea of Castle Rock.

These sherds add to the limited corpus of early Bronze Age material recorded from the Stirling area and augment the distribution of Food Vessels in Scotland. They also point to the possible location of an early Bronze Age site. In the absence of conclusive evidence in favour of either a domestic or funerary context, further investigation will be required to resolve the issue. Regardless of the nature of this site, this small assemblage provides some of the earliest evidence of human activity in Stirling.

Acknowledgements

Thanks are due to James K. Thomson, then Curator of the 'Smith', for permission to excavate and to the excavation team: Trevor Cox, Dorothy Milne, Dr J.C. ('Ian') Orkney, Eric Ross, Susan Ross and James K. Thomson. Ian Orkney generously shared his memories of the excavation, although responsibility for the interpretations presented here, and for any errors or omissions, is mine alone. I am grateful to Dr Neville Dix for his helpful editorial comments and patience. Yet again, I am indebted to my parents Norma and Jim, on this occasion for storing the sherds safely for so many years.

Bibliography

Aitchison, N. 2013. Later prehistoric pottery from the King's Park, Stirling, *The Forth Naturalist and Historian* **36**,149-60.

Aitken, P., Cunningham, C. and McCutcheon, B. 1984. *Notes for a New History of Stirling: Kings Park*, Stirling: the authors.

Cook, W.B. 1907. The King's Park of Stirling in history and record, *Stirling Natural History and Archaeological Society Transactions* 1906-07, 110-37.

Cowie, T.G. 1978. *Bronze Age Food Vessel Urns in Northern Britain*, BAR British Series 55, Oxford: British Archaeological Reports.

Crawford, O.G.S. 1949. *The Topography of Roman Scotland North of the Antonine Wall*, Cambridge: Cambridge University Press.

Digney, S. and Jones, R. 2013. Recent investigations at the King's Knot, Stirling, *The Forth Naturalist and Historian* **36**, 129-47.

Gibson, A. and Woods, A. 1997. *Prehistoric Pottery for the Archaeologist*, 2nd edn, Leicester: Leicester University Press.

Maitland, W. 1757. *The History and Antiquities of Scotland*, Vol. 1, London: A. Miller.

RCAHMS 1979. The Royal Commission on the Ancient and Historical Monuments of Scotland, *The Archaeological Sites and Monuments of Stirling District, Central Region*, The Archaeological Sites and Monuments of Scotland no. 7, Edinburgh: RCAHMS.

Roy. W. 1747-55. Military Survey of Scotland. Map images available at maps.nls.uk

Sheridan, A. 2003. New dates for Scottish Bronze Age cinerary urns: results from the National Museums of Scotland Dating Cremated Bones Project, in A. Gibson (ed.), *Prehistoric Pottery, People, Pattern and Purpose*, Prehistoric Ceramics Research Group Occasional Publication 4, British Archaeological Report International Series 1156, Oxford: Archaeopress, 201-26.

Sheridan, A. 2004. Scottish Food Vessel chronology revisited, in A. Gibson and A. Sheridan (eds), *From Sickles to Circles: Britain and Ireland at the Time of Stonehenge*, Stroud: Tempus, 243-69.

Figure 1. Sherd 1: the interior (left) and exterior (right) surfaces of the later prehistoric body sherd. The break was made deliberately soon after discovery to demonstrate to more sceptical members of the excavation team that this was pottery, not stone.

Figure 2. Sherd 2: the interior (left) and exterior (right) surfaces of the Food Vessel rim sherd.

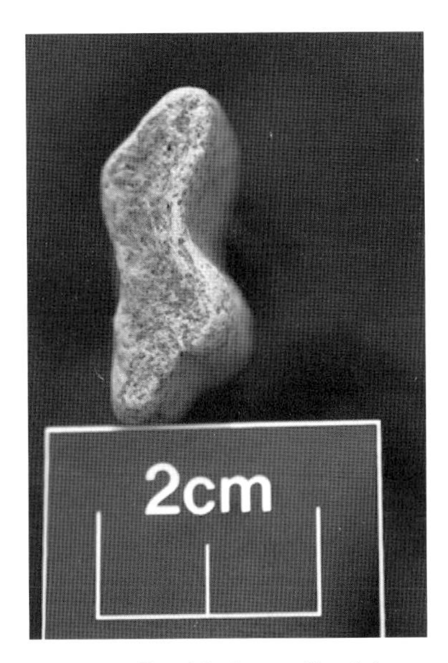

Figure 3. Sherd 2: the profile of the Food Vessel rim sherd, showing its darker core.

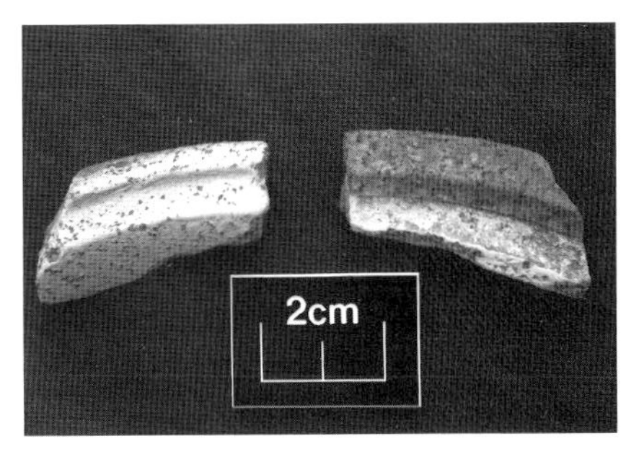

Figure 4. Sherd 3: the interior (left) and exterior (right) surfaces of the late Neolithic/early Bronze Age rim sherd.

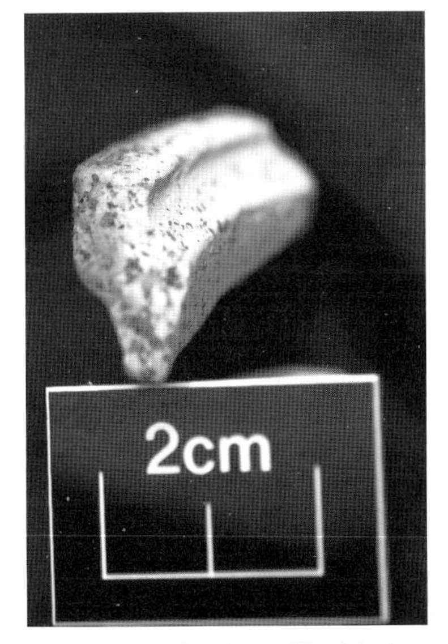

Figure 5. Sherd 3: the profile of the late Neolithic/early Bronze Age rim sherd, showing its darker core.

Figure 6. Sherd 4: the interior (left) and exterior (right) of the late Neolithic/early Bronze Age body sherd.

Report of the *Forth Naturalist and Historian* Man and the Landscape Conference Saturday November 16th 2013

The Changing Biodiversity of Central Scotland

To celebrate The Year of Natural Scotland, as well as the United Nations' Decade of Biodiversity, The Society held a major meeting to review changes in biodiversity over the last 50 years or so. The conference also served to highlight the achievements of the Society in its successful *What's Changed? Project: Measuring Biodiversity Change in the Forth Valley through Citizen Science*. The conference attracted more than 150 people.

The meeting was opened by Stirling University's Deputy Principal, Prof **Steve Burt**, who spoke about the aspirations that the University has for it's campus. Airthrey has been listed by Historic Scotland for its 18th century garden landscape. The diversity of habitats on campus is remarkable, and a local biodiversity plan is being formulated to enhance these. This is now aided by one of the FNH *What's Changed?* projects, when the Stirling University Nature Society conducted a 'bioblitz' of the campus in 2011 and 2012.

The Chair of the morning session was **Carol Evans** (Director for Scotland, Woodland Trust), who summarised the commitment of the Trust to protecting the ancient woodlands of the Forth region and fostering new native woodlands, with 90 sites covering some 9000 ha in Scotland. The Forth region is particularly well represented. Glen Finglas is by far the Trust's largest property at 5000 ha, an upland wood pasture managed for cattle and deer, and forming with the Forestry Commission property at Loch Katrine and the that at Inversnaid, held by the RSPB, an enormous area to develop landscape-scale policies. Glen Devon, at a little over 1,235 ha is the Trust's second largest property, acquired early in the 21st century with funding from the Scottish Forest Alliance, where the Trust has planted over 800 ha of native woodland. In a very different context, Livingston in West Lothian is an urban woodland project, tremendously important for urban wildlife and part of the habitat networks which are a fundamental aspect of the Central Scotland Green Network (CSGN).

Carol introduced **Ed Mackey** (Scottish Natural Heritage): who spoke about Central Scotland and its changing environment. He began with success stories, with the re-colonisation of otter to central Scotland and land management for the Great Crested Newt. Central Scotland is at the edge of the newt's range, and so under-represented from traditional surveys in the National Biological Network (NBN), but environmental DNA tracing (eDNA) has proved effective in establishing presence, and is faster, requires less skill and has a low error rate. Great Crested Newt has now been established as native much further north than the Forth. He reviewed the ambitions of the CSGN, connecting spaces in towns and cities with the countryside and coast, with every settlement in central Scotland within good-quality landscape by 2050. He introduced the NBN Gateway (https://data.nbn.org.uk), the inter-active web-site for Scotland's biodiversity, and the Scotland's environment site: (http://www.environment.scotland.gov.uk), also fully inter-active and a great store of maps, tools and data.

Peter Maitland (Fish Conservation Centre: SavingFish@sky.com) considered the changing fish fauna of central Scotland. He took us back to the last Ice Age in Scotland, when there were no fish. They arrived 12,000 years ago. The Arctic Charr arrived then, the most northerly freshwater fish anywhere in the world. There are now three populations, one of which is in Loch Lubnaig. There are 42 freshwater species of fish, 40 in central Scotland, 26 native and 16 alien species. Perhaps most iconic is the Atlantic Salmon which, Maitland argued, has a stable population in the River Forth. The Brown Trout population is very robust but Sparling numbers are declining, though, from over-fishing. Eel populations have collapsed globally since the mid-1960s. While Vendace have become extinct, there is now a re-stocking programme in Loch Skeen, high in the Southern Uplands. The re-introduction of Powan into Loch Lomond was described by Peter in Volume 36 of the FNH Journal. It has been stocked in Loch Sloy and the Carron Reservoir. Loch Lomond and the Forth are homes to the only Scottish populations of freshwater feeding Lampreys.

Grayling, an alien species, is known as the 'queen of the river'. In the late 19th century it was found only in the Clyde, Tweed and Nith, but by 1970 it was common in all three, and in the Tay, and is now common throughout southern Scotland. The Ruffe is also alien. In Loch Lomond it is trapped and monitored at Ross Priory. There has been a huge and unwanted increase in the population since 1990. We need to stop new alien introductions, Maitland concluded, through improved legislation. Native species need protection, and management plans that are holistic in ambition.

Buglife contributed enormously to the success of the FNH *What's Changed?* Project. **Scott Shanks** discussed changes to central Scotland's butterflies, moths and other invertebrates. There are more than 40,000 species of invertebrates in the UK, 26,000 in Scotland. In fact, some 85 % of Scotland's biodiversity is invertebrate. Their activities include pollination, soil management, nutrient cycling, waste management, natural controls of pests, and providing food for us and other animals.

Invertebrate surveys can be problematic with 26,000 species, and few expert recorders. But butterfly and moth data are invaluable in monitoring changes in biodiversity. Butterflies, for instance, react rapidly to environmental changes and so are good indicators of habitat quality. They are also relatively straight forward to identify. Survey techniques have now been formalised, with timed counts and walked transects. The Butterfly Monitoring scheme, established in

1976, merged with the UK Butterfly Monitoring Scheme network in 2006, and now some 1076 sites are monitored, 55 in Scotland. Regular monitoring allows the identification of new arrivals, species decline and competition for resources. We can differentiate between 'generalist' and 'specialist' feeders. Since 1979, generalist feeders are increasing at the expense of specialists.

Habitat management is helping some species, such as the Pearl-bordered Fritillary. But habitat loss is important at a local scale, as Stirling University Nature Society demonstrated in the Forth region. Climate change is helping several species, as seen in increases in Red Admiral and Painted Lady while spring species flying earlier in the year. The population trend for 24 of the 33 species of butterfly is that 13 are increasing, six significantly, and 11 are decreasing, only one significantly so. Southern species are expanding their range northward since 1990. The Orange Tip was found in the Lothians and the Solway Firth in the 1970s, expanding from there by the 1980s, and to almost all 10 km squares of Scotland south of the Forth-Clyde line in the 1990s. The Comma, the subject of one of the FNH *What's Changed* projects, colonised a few squares south of the Forth-Clyde line in the 1990s, spreading up the east coast to Angus in the early 21st century and Perthshire by 2010. The abundance of moths has declined in southern Britain since 1965, but is holding steady in Scotland. Among the aquatic invertebrates, Dragonfly and damselfly populations are increasing. Six new species of hoverfly were recorded in a FNH-sponsored *What's Changed* survey of two 10 km squares. Aliens remain a problem. The New Zealand flatworm has spread from the Edinburgh Botanic Gardens from their accidental introduction in 1965. The New Zealand flatworm affects populations of moles because it eats worms.

Jonny Hughes (Director of Conservation, SWT) introduced the afternoon speakers, but asked the audience to focus on the restoration of biodiversity, through greater connectivity of habitats, to diversified land uses, and to urban environments that are pro-nature. **John Haddow** is a free-lance consultant (Auritus Wildlife Consultancy@ auritus@btinternet.com) and an expert on mammals in central Scotland. We have 36 mammals in Scotland. He focused on changing geographical patterns in two. The Water Vole (*Arvicola amphibius*) has been the subject of a major release programme in the last few years at the Forestry Commission Loch Ard Forest, which included the creation of new ponds and habitat restoration. Expansion of the population also required the systematic trapping of American Mink, another alien. The expansion of the range of Pine Marten (*Martes martes*) is even more successful. Confined to the central and north west Highlands until the 1990s, it has expanded to eastern and central Scotland, from environmental DNA markers and droppings (scats). There is even a local hotspot around the Airthrey Estate.

Roy Sexton (SWT and FNH) then evaluated changes in the floral biodiversity of central Scotland over the last *c.* 40 years. His baseline was a 1971 paper by John Proctor: *Vegetation and Flora of Central Scotland*, in Timms' edited volume on *The Stirling Region*. Central Scotland has a very rich flora of 1500 species of flowering plants. The arctic-alpine and montane flora of the NTS-owned estate on Ben Lawers is internationally important, with 16 Red Data Book species and 56 nationally scarce species. Threats to this flora are from sheep grazing: too little or too much, with the balance very delicate. Sheep and deer exclosures from 1987 have been a spectacular success here.

Climate change may be leading to the loss of snow-patch species. Closer to Stirling, Sticky catchfly is our most outstanding plant, with the biggest population in the UK on the cliffs and screes of the Ochils, the subject of one FNH-sponsored *What's Changed* re-survey in 2013.

The Forth valley raised mosses are a very special habitat and home to a number of Red Data Book species. Originally there were 95,000 hectares of raised bog in the UK of which only 6,000 hectares remain. In 1972 Flanders Moss was being drained for horticultural peat extraction and forestry. SWT purchased part of the site and stopped the development. Later SNH bought out the extraction rights for £1.3 m and it is now a National Nature Reserve. Wester Moss at Fallin has now become a Butterfly Conservation Nature Reserve while Shirgarton and Killorn Mosses have had birch woodlands removed by SNH to restore the habitat. The biodiversity of wetland habitats is high. Scottish Dock (*Rumex aquaticus*), for instance, has an almost circum-polar distribution but in the British Isles it is only found at Balmaha on Loch Lomond side and on the flood plain of the Endrick. Some woodland herbs like Bluebell and Wild Garlic have flourished. Threats to the woodland ground flora come from *Rhododendron ponticum*, Spanish Bluebell, deer and a lack of management. Some 70 % of central Scotland is cultivated or grazed grassland. Some arable weeds like Corn Marigold, Poppy, Scentless Mayweed, Hemp-nettle etc have long lived seed banks in the soil, and set-aside has given them the chance to germinate once more. Grassland 'improvement' has resulted in a massive loss of wild flower-rich grasslands through construction, overgrazing or abandonment, afforestation and leisure activities. Fortunately a few unimproved grasslands like Quoigs Meadow remain, many partially protected by designating them as SSSIs.

Ben Darvill (British Trust for Ornithology) evaluated data obtained from the publication of the *Bird Atlas 2007-11*. Our landscape and land uses are changing, in farming, forestry, energy generation, disturbance, recreation and muirburn frequency. Our climate is also changing. Bird atlases provide periodic insights into the status of all of bird species in an area. The first UK breeding bird atlas was for 1968-72. The 1988-91 *The Bird Atlas* allowed us to see changes in bird distributions for the first time. Declines in farmland birds became the focus of much research. The 2008-11 *The Bird Atlas* recorded populations in 2 km x 2 km squares, sampled twice in summer and twice in winter. It has over 16 million records of 520 species (and subspecies), with over 3,870 10 km squares surveyed, involving 40,000 observers.

Woodland, farmland, wetland and upland birds show positive change in our region while wading birds show negative change. Migrants are faring badly south of the Anglo-Scots border but show positive trends in Scotland. Within species, Siskin is increasing as conifer plantations mature, Jays and Ravens also because fewer people are shooting them nowadays, and the Nuthatch is moving north through climate change, and Greylag Geese populations are soaring because their habitat was under-utilised. On the other hand, Corn Bunting abundance is falling, pinned to the east coast and the Uists. Causes of change are often complex and multiple. For instance, Willow Warblers are at the southern edge of their breeding range. They have lower survival rates and lower breeding success than in England, through climate and land use change. In Scotland, reductions in grazing pressures, especially from sheep (due to changes to agricultural subsidies under the CAP) but also from deer in some areas, and increases in scrub and young woodland due to enlightened management, help to maintain and expand bird populations. It was argued that we need to model predictions of how land use changes will effect Scottish birds but we have few sites where they are needed – in the uplands. We also need more recorders. The BTO web-site (www.birdtrack.net) encourages contributions, as does the Breeding Bird Survey. (www.bto.org/volunteer-surveys/bbs)

Duncan Orr Ewing (RSPB) followed with an analysis of the changing fortunes of Central Scotland's raptors. He introduced the Central Scotland Raptor Study Group, which co-ordinates monitoring across the region and contributes to the Scottish Raptor Monitoring Scheme. Trends are shown in this table.

Species	**No of breeding pairs**	**Trend**
Golden eagles	10	Stable
Red Kite	27	Increasing slowly
Osprey	20	Increasing
Goshawk	3	Increasing slowly
Sparrowhawk	Not known	Not known
Buzzard	c200 pairs monitored	Stable
Kestrel	Not known	Declining fast
Peregrine	26 monitored (some sites not checked)	Declining slowly
Merlin	c10	Stable
Hen harrier	c5-10	Stable/declining
Short-eared owl	c5-10	Stable/declining
Long-eared owl	4	Unknown
Tawny owl	31 pairs monitored	Stable? Hard winter
Barn owl	32 pairs monitored	Stable? Hard winter
Raven	72 pairs monitored	Increasing

It was left to the Chair of FNH, **Michael Usher**, to summarise the day. There exist Biodiversity Action Plans at all spatial scales, from very local to global.

Scottish Natural Heritage has, for its part, defined its strategy for the conservation and enhancement of biodiversity to 2020. Action plans cost money, however, while public sector expenditure on biodiversity in the UK rose from *c.* £280 million in 2000-1 to peak at nearly £600 million in 2008-9, around 0.4 % of GDP. The 'crash' has forced a decline in spending from 2010-11. Is biodiversity now seen to be too expensive? Or can we afford not to protect and enhance it?

Richard Tipping

WHAT FACTORS HAVE HAD THE MOST IMPACT ON CENTRAL SCOTLAND'S BIODIVERSITY DURING THE LAST 30 YEARS ?

Stirling Members Centre of the Scottish Wildlife Trust

As part of the *Year of Natural Scotland* the annual Forth Naturalist and Historian Conference of 2013 was dedicated to *The Changing Biodiversity of Central Scotland*. The theme proved a great success and the meeting was attended by 150 naturalists. As part of their contribution, Stirling Members Centre of the Scottish Wildlife Trust decided to conduct a survey of these 'mud on their boots' naturalists to find out what they thought had been the factors that had had the most negative and positive impacts on local wildlife over the last 30 years.

To make the survey manageable it was decided to ask those taking part to select three choices from lists of twelve potential negative and positive impacts compiled from suggestions submitted by experienced field naturalists. Attendees could either opt to complete the questionnaire on line before the conference or fill in a paper copy on the day. Having worried about whether enough delegates would take part to make the data meaningful the organisers were taken aback by the enthusiasm of all those present and had to send out for extra copies of the questionnaire sheet. Eventually 151 surveys were completed, far more than had been anticipated. A team of SWT members managed to collate these submissions so that the results could be presented before the close of the conference (Table 1).

The factor that was judged to have the most detrimental impact on wildlife was the intensification of agriculture driven by the Common Agricultural Policy. The conference speaker who addressed the changes in the flora of Central Scotland gave a number of examples including widespread use of selective herbicides which had resulted in the loss of wildflower rich meadows and arable field species like cornflowers, corncockles and chicory. The impact of overgrazing was also illustrated by the spectacular growth of mountain plants on areas of Ben Lawers National Nature Reserve that had been fenced to exclude sheep. The loss of wildflowers in turn reduces the numbers of invertebrates like butterflies and bumble bees that are dependent on them and efforts to mitigate these impacts were being made by planting wildflower verges. Similarly a number of farmland birds like corn buntings and corncrakes are believed to have become locally extinct as a result of changes in agricultural practice.

Table 1. The factors that were thought to have had the most negative impact on local wildlife over the last 30 years. Votes cast on left

Votes	Factor
91	**Intensification of agriculture** through the use of herbicides, pesticides, fertilisers and more powerful machinery, in conjunction with a supportive Common Agricultural Policy
74	**The spread of invasive alien species** e.g. grey squirrel, mink, signal crayfish, Dutch elm disease, giant hogweed, New Zealand flatworm, etc.
59	**Short-termism in conservation** ... the duration and funding of many projects is too short to be effective
50	**Poor management of wildlife rich marginal land** such as hedgerows, field margins, road verges and ditches
34	**The impact of major infrastructure projects** like wind farms, pylon lines, motorways, gas extraction, major bridges, new towns and villages
30	**Climate change**
27	**Lack of native wildlife education** from primary schools to undergraduate courses at Universities.
24	**Persecution of native wildlife** (raptors, badgers, otters, hares, foxes, water fowl, etc.) by gaming interests
21	**Disturbance created by increased uninformed human and canine access to the countryside** including outdoor pursuits like climbing, mountain biking, power boating, hiking.
18	**The poor implementation of Local Biodiversity Action Plans**
11	**The lack of a Wildlife Recording Centre to inform local planning decisions**
7	**Negative impacts on our migratory species originating abroad**

The second most adverse effect was perceived to be the spread of invasive non-native species. All the conference speakers who were charged with reviewing the changes in the biodiversity of specific wildlife groups gave examples. The wild-mammal expert discussed the impact of American mink and grey squirrels on native water vole and red squirrel populations. The speaker covering invertebrates dealt with the adverse effects of New Zealand flat worms, signal crayfish and harlequin ladybirds. The fish expert described the disastrous consequences of introduced ruffe on Loch Lomond's native powan population and the botanist illustrated the massive impact of Dutch elm disease, ash die back, giant hogweed, Himalayan balsam and skunk cabbage and complained about the lack of an effective national biosecurity policy.

In third place was the effect of 'short termism' in conservation. Policies and programmes seemed to be constantly changing and the duration of funding (1-3 years) was usually too short to complete projects. This has the unfortunate side effect of generating a rapid turn-over of staff who are often only just reaching peak effectiveness when their employment is terminated. Marginal land such as hedgerows, field margins, road verges and ditches are considered to be potentially valuable refuges for many persecuted species. Sadly little thought seems to be given to their management for wildlife. Hedgerows and verges are cut much more frequently than is optimal for wildlife and increasingly drainage ditches (with all the biodiversity they contain) are being replaced by underground permeable plastic conduits sunk in beds of ballast. The impact of major infrastructure projects like windfarms, pylon lines, gas extraction, new trunk roads, major bridges, new villages, etc. only ranked fifth. This was an unexpected result in view of the extensive press coverage given to their potential adverse effects.

Several of our Local Biodiversity Action Plans suggest that Climate Change is the single biggest issue facing us when we look to conserve existing biodiversity. It is usually not clear where such judgements originate but they are important in steering conservation policy. At least when considering the past 30 years, Central Scotland's field naturalists seemed to disagree and placed climate change as 6th most important factor in their ratings. Although there is constant speculation that loss or gain of species might be due to changing climate, such claims are very difficult to substantiate. For instance during the conference the case of the reduction in alpine gentian numbers on Ben Lawers was discussed. This has been attributed to a climate induced increased growth of competing grasses but might equally be the effect of changing grazing patterns.

Top of the list of factors that had a positive impact on wildlife was environmental legislation like that which resulted in the reduction of the pollution of rivers, the cleaning up of the atmosphere (acid rain) and the banning of organochlorine pesticides (81 votes). Second was the influence of conservation organisations like the SWT, NTS, RSPB, Woodland Trust etc. (67 votes). Third with 54 votes was the improved public awareness of wildlife conservation issues as a consequence of the efforts of the media (e.g. Springwatch and Landward TV programmes) and wildlife organisations. International treaty obligations such as the Rio Convention on Biological Diversity, the Ramsar Convention, the European Habitat and Species Directive and the EC Birds Directive with 47 votes was fourth followed by Lottery and Landfill Tax Grants which fund wildlife conservation projects (39 votes). In joint 5th place was the increased effectiveness of wildlife monitoring which provides the scientific underpinning for the development of conservation policy. Factors included the recruitment of more recorders, the use of GPS and tracking systems, better field guides, on-line wildlife identification services, digital cameras, internet based record submission etc.

In the space available for comments on the questionnaire, by far the most frequent response was the difficulty those participating had in ranking these factors … a common view was that they were all very important!

Roy Sexton

GIANT HOGWEED BY THE RIVER ALLAN AND THE UPPER FORTH: CHARTING THE CHANGE 1985-2013

Guy Harewood

In 1985 a survey of Giant Hogweed (*Heracleum mantegazzianum*) along the banks of the River Allan and part of the River Forth was carried out by Stirling University (R. Neiland, J. Proctor and R. Sexton) and published in Volume 9 of *Forth Naturalist and Historian* (FNH) Journal. At this time the danger that this alien species with its toxic sap could overwhelm our river banks was beginning to be appreciated and the survey showed colonies were already established all the way downstream from Greenloaning to Cambuskenneth.

Last summer FNH obtained a grant from Scottish Natural Heritage (SNH) as part of the *What's Changed Project* to repeat the 1985 survey and establish whether giant hogweed had spread or been held in check. Local Countryside Rangers Guy Harewood and Claire Bird led the project with the assistance of ten volunteers. The survey was conducted using a similar methodology to that employed in 1985 allowing changes in the distribution during the intervening 28 years to be accurately charted.

Giant Hogweeed is a native of the Caucasus Mountains in Russia and was introduced into England as a garden plant in 1817. By 1828 it was reported growing wild in Cambridgeshire and since then it has become widespread throughout the UK including Scotland. It may have been introduced into the Stirling area by a stream which drains into the River Allan from the gardens of Cromlix House (NN 785 059) where it is known to have been planted in the first decade of the last century (Neiland et al, 1985).

Ecology

As its name implies, giant hogweed grows tall, with mature plants reaching 3-5 metres in height and leaves over a metre wide. It has a large umbel of up to 60,000 small white flowers allowing up to 120,000 small, paper thin seeds to be produced per plant (Dodd et al, 1994). An average plant bears about 20,000 seeds, but individual plants with over 100,000 seeds have been reported (Nielsen et al, 2005). One study in the Czech Republic cited a 3.3 metre tall giant hogweed plant which produced 107,984 seeds (Caffrey, 1999). In the ground seeds can stay dormant for up to 7 years because they contain a rich and abundant food store (Andersen, 1994). However, Moravcová et al (2007) reported that only 1.2 % of the seeds in their study remained viable after 3 years of burial. Although there is some dispute over the precise length of time that seeds remain viable it is clear that there is a huge seed bank. For example, in a stand of 50 plants approximately 1,000,000 seeds will be produced each year.

Giant hogweed plants are monocarpic. They grow for several years, usually flowering in the third to fifth year after which they set seed and die. In unfavourable conditions such as on nutrient poor, shaded or dry sites or those that are regularly grazed, flowering is postponed until sufficient reserves have been accumulated. In such conditions, plants can live for at least 12 years (Nielsen et al, 2005).

Being small and light giant hogweed seeds are easily dispersed. They can be carried 10 to 50 m from the parent plant by the wind (Caffrey, 1994). Studies of individuals about 2 m tall show that 60-90 % of seeds fall on the ground within a radius of 4 m of the parent plant; the density of seeds declining rapidly with increasing distance from the source (Nielsen et al, 2005). Clegg and Grace (1974) and Dawe and White (1979) (cited by Moravcová et al 2007) also report that giant hogweed seeds have the ability to float for up to 3 days. Therefore, when water is the primary dispersal route, such as in riparian or coastal zones or areas prone to flooding, there is the potential for seeds to move over huge distances.

Seeds normally result from cross fertilisation between two different plants but there can be an overlap in the formation of male and female flowers in a single umbel, which makes self-fertilization possible. This means that even a single isolated plant is capable of founding a new population (Nielsen et al, 2005).

Impacts and control

The continued spread of this plant is a cause of great concern because of its impact on human health and on the ecology of infested areas (Caffrey, 2001).

The plant's enormous size, immense seed production and ability to survive in a variety of habitats and conditions helps it out-compete our native plants. As a result it ultimately produces large dense stands in which most other species are virtually excluded. Being the largest forb in central Europe its large leaves allow it to intercept most of the available light (Pysek, 1994) and in dominant stands up to 80 % of the incoming light is absorbed (Nielsen et al, 2005). As a consequence little or no light reaches the surrounding vegetation which ultimately dies.

In the autumn, giant hogweed loses its huge leaves keeping only the stalk. Since few other plants can survive under its canopy the soil is left open and vulnerable to wind and water erosion (Dodd et al, 1994). The Tweed Forum (2006) has been involved in a systematic attempt to eradicate giant hogweed along the River Tweed. They have observed that after producing seed the large, deep tap-root dies and rots to leave a hole up to 15 cm across and 30 cm deep. Within dense stands there can be several thousand plants in a 100 m stretch of river bank. The perforation caused by root rotting together with a lack of any vegetation sward and associated root mat results in the soil being exposed to the full erosive force of the river and whole sections of riverbank can disappear during peak flows.

Giant hogweed also poses a health and safety risk. The plant exudes a sap, which contains several photosensitizing furanocoumarins. In contact with the human skin and in combination with ultraviolet radiation, these compounds cause blistering of the skin (Nielsen et al, 2005). Local instances have occurred involving children playing at the water's edge in Bridge of Allan and estate workers trying to clear the plant from the banks. .

In some of the worst affected areas the plants can form an almost impenetrable barrier preventing access to the river for both fishing and other recreation use; so the economic impacts of this invasive plant cannot be overlooked.

A number of methods are currently employed to try to control, and ultimately halt, the plant's spread. Manual and mechanical methods include root cutting, mowing, cutting the plant, and umbel removal. With the exception of root cutting, these methods do not immediately kill the plants. Death occurs ultimately as a result of the depletion of the plants nutrient reserves and requires two to three treatments per year during several growing seasons (Nielsen et al, 2005).

Chemical control of giant hogweed, using systemic herbicides such as glyphosate and triclopyr, has proved both effective and cheap. The plant is also readily grazed by sheep and cows which appear to suffer no ill-effects. This has proved to be very effective method of control (Nielsen et al, 2005) and some grazed fields in heavily infested areas can remain virtually free of the plant.

Thiele and Otte (2006) describe the primary factors that constrain giant hogweed establishment as land usage, shading and low-productive site conditions. They also state that the majority of invaded sites have been subject to human related habitat changes, with the most important process being land-use decline or abandonment. Land management is therefore a viable control mechanism as giant hogweed cannot readily establish in areas of well managed land such as farmland and parkland. Although the Allan Water and River Forth do pass through much agricultural land, riverbanks are often fenced or left unploughed and therefore provide a suitable unmanaged habitat for the plant.

Any effective control programme needs to be both in place for many years and also to have the active participation of all the land owners. The Tweed Forum (2014) has demonstrated that this is possible and report that after 10 years of catchment-wide control, giant hogweed coverage is greatly reduced. All plants in the project area have been prevented from flowering during this period which should result in a reduction in the seed bank and eventual eradication.

Survey methodology

The 1985 survey mapped the giant hogweed up to 50 m from the water's edge on the banks of the River Allan and a section of the River Forth downstream from its confluence with the Allan to Stirling Bridge. The survey started from the A822 road bridge over the Allan Water north of Greenloaning (NN 835 079) and finished at the footbridge over the River Forth between Riverside and Cambuskenneth (NS 805 940). It was conducted over 5 days between 3rd and 24th August. To be broadly consistent with this the follow-up 2013 survey was carried out on the between 14th-20th August. Where possible the number of adult and immature plants were counted and their position captured using a hand-held GPS. Where they were too numerous the estimated numbers and density of mature plants was recorded using a classification system comparable to the original survey. If the stands where too large to record with a single GPS coordinate the area of the colony was recorded using GPS coordinates at the start and end of the stand.

The survey was conducted by groups of volunteers each led by a Countryside Ranger who briefed the group on the survey methodology and the identification of invasive non-native species. Japanese knotweed, Himalayan balsam and American skunk cabbage were also recorded.

Comparison with 1985

The data showed that along the upper reaches of the Allan from Greenloaning down to Cromlix there were only a few individual flowering giant hogweed plants (Figure 1) in contrast to 1985 when there had been 12 colonies each with more than 50 mature plants. However in some areas the banks were still covered in young immature plants. This pattern resulted from the death of older plants as a result of herbicide application and grazing by sheep and cattle. During 2013 the River Forth Fisheries Trust (RFFT) were in the first year of a systematic eradication programme. Together with their volunteer sprayers they worked down from Geenloaning to Cromlix during the spring and summer killing off the older plants and leaving the seedlings. They will return in 2014 to kill the regrowth. In addition many areas were subject to grazing up to the water's edge and the only mature plants found here were on inaccessible slopes.

By contrast the region from Cromlix down past Kinbuck to Dunblane where the banks originally carried only three colonies of flowering plants there are now massive forests occupying hundreds of metres of bank particularly downstream of Ashfield. There had also been similar major increases between Dunblane and Bridge of Allan. In these sections there are long stretches where the river runs through steep inaccessible wooded gorges. There is little or no grazing and where farmland occurs along the banks it supports arable crops where ploughing does not extend to the water's edge. This allows the survival of plants along the banks. These factors together with the absence of any

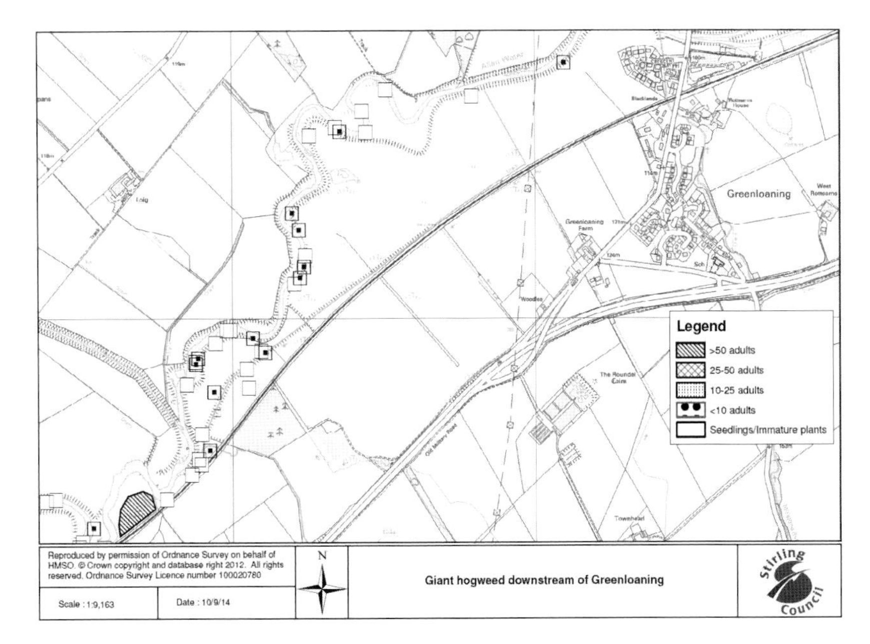

Figure 1. In 1984 there were 12 giant hogweed colonies each with more than 50 mature plants along this stretch of bank downstream of Greenloaning. By 2013 grazing and herbicide treatment had significantly reduced the number of flowering plants but there were still large numbers of seedlings.

systematic chemical control has allowed the giant hogweed to flourish and grow unchecked.

In the 1985 survey the biggest giant hogweed stand was near the Cornton level crossing (NS 789 963). It occupied the derelict Pig Testing Station (now a housing estate) and the adjacent land where Cornton Prison now stands (Figure 2). This stand has been partially eradicated by the development of the site and grazing on the remaining fields but unfortunately the colony has spread to the opposite bank and forms a continuous dense stand from the rail bridge all the way down to the Forth (Figure 2).

The stretch down the River Forth from its junction with the Allan to Cambuskenneth had six small colonies in 1985. Some of these behind the Causewayhead Rd have expanded into major colonies and there is now an almost continuous dense stand from the rail bridge through the rugby club and up to the Ladysneuk Rd to Cambuskenneth. A continuous spraying programme by the Stirling Council fisheries team has all but eliminated mature plants from the opposite side of the river through Raploch and Riverside.

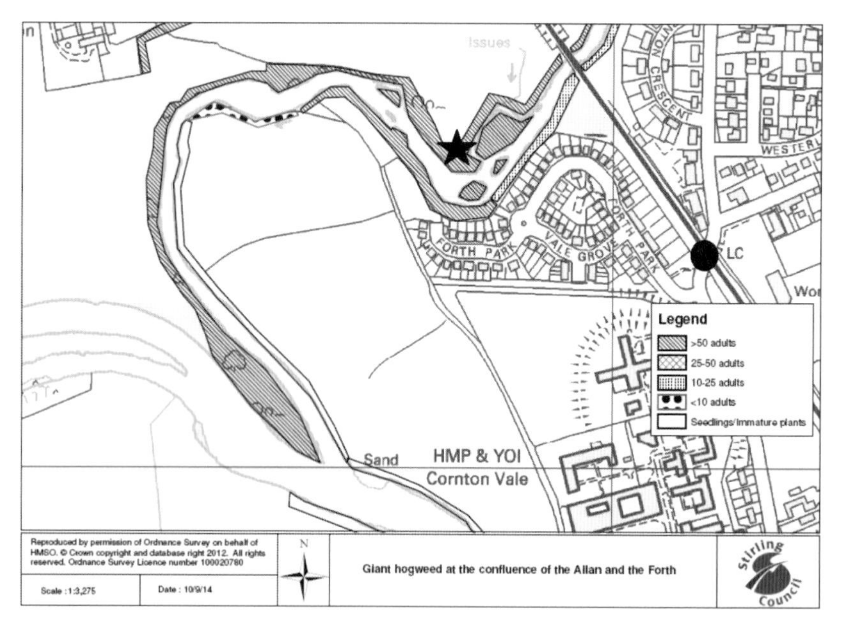

Figure 2. In the 1985 survey the biggest colony of giant hogweed was near the Cornton level crossing (dot). By 2013 this stand has been partially eradicated by the development of the site and grazing on the remaining fields. Unfortunately the giant hogweed has spread to the opposite bank (star) and forms a continuous dense stand from the rail bridge all the way down to the Forth.

The 1985 survey states that *plants were occasionally seen on roadside verges and railway lines close to the rivers* and that one individual was seen about 1 km from the river. The situation is much worse now with giant hogweed found along the majority of the rail line between Stirling and Dunblane as well as along many of the roads around Stirling. It is no longer confined to the river corridor and is well established throughout the Stirling area.

The Neiland et al. survey states that *at most sites where adults were present there were less than 50 flowering plants… the largest colony was in Bridge of Allan where there were many hundreds of adults.* In 2013 there were a large number of areas that each contained many hundreds of flowering plants. In some sites around Dunblane and Bridge of Allan the plants were too numerous to accurately estimate.

In summary these results show that there has been a major increase in the number of giant hogweed plants in many areas. There has also been a significant decrease in areas where effective treatment programmes have been in place and where there is grazing, by cattle and sheep.

Over the intervening years from 1985-2013 a number of attempts have been made to control the plant, some at a very local level and some in a more systematic way. The Clackmannanshire and Stirling Environment Trust (CSET) funded control efforts during 2004, 2006, 2007, 2008 and 2009, with spraying undertaken along the Allan Water stretching from Greenloaning to its confluence with the River Forth. All plants within 6 m of the water's edge were treated. The CSET report (2011) stated that *the dedicated spraying program has had a significant affect on the level of invasive weeds along the Allan Water*. The treatment reduced the number of colonies of mature plants but led to an increase in the number of seedlings and immature plants. This is likely to be due to the increased light available in the absence of mature plants (Morrison, 2011).

As described above RFFT undertook treatment of giant hogweed between Greenloaning and Kinbuck in 2013 and plan to treat the full length of the Allan in 2014, By eliminating the upstream seed sources before moving downstream they hope to eventually eradicate the plant. Unfortunately the long term funding for this Forth Invasive Non-Native Species (FINNS) programme is uncertain and is only currently guaranteed until the end of 2014. In addition to the control measures undertaken through CSET and RFFT local volunteers have been trained in herbicide application and will undertake future spraying in some areas.

The data gathered by this survey shows that despite the investment of £10,000 and thousands of volunteer hours the short-term or non-systematic nature of 30 years of management efforts has resulted in a failure to contain giant hogweed. Due to the plant's growth characteristics a long-term control and eradication plan is essential. The experience of the Tweed Forum (2014) suggests that it takes 10 years to be effective, so there is every likelihood that all these current control efforts will prove in vain unless the spraying programme is repeated annually as new seeds germinate.

All current and planned efforts focus on the river corridors, with little or no consideration for the wider landscape and the avenues for reinvasion from road or rail networks. It will prove almost impossible to eradicate the plant if a seed source exists nearby. The wider you look to control the plant the more complicated the problem becomes with multiple landowners and land managers involved.

To paraphrase the closing paragraph of Neiland et al (1985) '*If Giant Hogweed is to be controlled then a coordinated strategy aimed at eradicating all the colonies is needed, not just those on land owned by any single landowner. Controlling the plants must be maintained over several years to be effective, and this requires long-term planning by the local authorities, landowners and other stakeholders*'. This statement is still as true today as it was nearly 30 years ago.

Figure 3. Volunteer Niall Currie in a dense stand of giant hogweed in 2013 a few metres from the site of the largest stand recorded in 1985.

Acknowledgements

Thanks go to Claire Bird (Stirling Council Ranger Service) and Roy Sexton for their help organising and conducting this survey and to Jonathan Louis (RFFT) and Audrey Morrison (CSET) for providing information. Thanks also go to all the volunteers who took part and without whom this survey would not have been possible; Colin Abercrombie, Roy Anderson, Chris Calder, Niall Currie, Bill Greasley, Jan Harbridge, Bill Jack, Iain Kirkman, Tony Rogers and Steve Wilkinson.

References

Andersen, U.V. 1994. Sheep grazing as a method of controlling *Heracleum mantegazzianum*. In Waal, L.C., Child, L.E., Wade, P.M., and Brock, J.H. Eds pages 77-92. *Ecology and Management of Invasive Riverside Plants*. West Sussex, England: John Wiley & Sons Ltd.

Caffrey, J.M. 1994. Spread and management of *Heracleum mantegazzianum* along the Irish river corridors. In Waal, L.C., Child, L.E., Wade, P.M., and Brock, J.H. Eds pages 67-76. *Ecology and Management of Invasive Riverside Plants*. West Sussex, England: John Wiley & Sons Ltd,.

Caffery, J.M. 1999. Phenology and long-term control of *Heracleum mantegazzianum*. *Hydrobiologia* **415**, 223-228.

Caffrey, J. 2001. The Management of Giant Hogweed in an Irish River Catchment *Journal of Aquatic. Plant Management* **39**, 28-33.

Clegg, L.M. and Grace, J. 1974. The distribution of *Heracleum mantegazzianum* (Somm. & Levier) near Edinburgh. *Transactions of the Botanical Society of Edinburgh* **42**, 223–229.

Dawe, N.K. and White, E.R. 1979 Giant Cow Parsnip (*Heracleum mantegazzianum*) on Vancouver Island, British Columbia. *Canadian Field Naturalist* **93**, 82–83.

Dodd, F.S., de Waal, L.C., Wade, P.M., and Tiley, G.E.D. 1994. Control and management of *Heracleum mantegazzianum*. In Waal, L.C., Child, L.E., Wade, P.M., and Brock, J.H. Eds. pages 111-126 *Ecology and Management of Invasive Riverside Plants*. West Sussex, England: John Wiley & Sons Ltd.

Mayer and LaRessa, K. 2000. Comparison of Management Techniques for *Heracleum mantegazzianum* in North and Central Europe. Restoration and Reclaimation Review, Dept of Horticultural Science, University of Minnesota.

Moravcová, L., Pyšek, P., Krinke, L., Pergl, J., Perglová, I. & Thompson, K. 2007: Seed germination, dispersal and seed bank in *Heracleum mantegazzianum*. In Pyšek P., Cock M.J.W., Nentwig W. & Ravn H.P. (Eds.*), Ecology and Management of Giant Hogweed (Heracleum mantegazzianum)*, CAB International, pp 74-91.

Morrison, A. 2011. The Stirling Invasive Weeds Project. Clackmannanshire and Stirling Environment Trust report (unpublished).

Neiland. R., Proctor, J. and Sexton, R. 1985. Giant hogweed *(Heracleum matnegazzianum)* by the River Allan and part of the River Forth. *The Forth Naturalist and Historian* **9**, 51-56.

Nielsen, C., Ravn, H.P., Nentwig, W. and Wade, M. (Eds.), 2005. The Giant Hogweed Best Practice Manual. Guidelines for the management and control of an invasive weed in Europe. Forest & Landscape Denmark, Hoersholm, 44 pp.

Pysek, P. 1994. Ecological aspects of invasion by *Heracleum mantegazzianum* in the Czech republic. In Waal, L.C., Child, L.E., Wade, P.M., and Brock, J.H. Eds. pages 45-54 *Ecology and Management of Invasive Riverside Plants*. West Sussex, England: John Wiley & Sons Ltd.

Thiele, J. and Otte, A., 2006. Analysis of habitats and communities invaded by *Heracleum mantegazzianum* Somm. et Lev. (Giant Hogweed) in Germany. *Phytocoenologia*, **36**, 281-320.

Tweed Forum 2006. The long-term control of Giant Hogweed and Japanese Knotweed [Online]. Available from: http://www.tweedforum.org/publications/tweed-invasives [Accessed 16/06/14].

Tweed Forum 2014. Tweed Invasives Project - progress to date [Online]. Available from: http://www.tweedforum.org/projects/current-projects/invasives_progress-to_date [Accessed 16/06/14].

TAILEND MOSS - A 30 YEAR INVESTIGATION OF THE AQUATIC INVERTEBRATE FAUNA

Craig Macadam

Tailend Moss is an area of lowland raised bog near Livingston, West Lothian. The site is owned by West Lothian Council and managed by the Scottish Wildlife Trust. The aquatic invertebrate fauna of bog pools on Tailend Moss was first investigated in 1983 (Richardson and Shiells, 1984). The current study resurveyed the pools in 2013 as part of the FNH *What's Changed* project, and investigates the changes in the invertebrate fauna over a 30 year period.

The methods used during this survey were based upon the British National Pond Survey (NPS) and the Predictive System for Multimetrics (PSYM) methodology to ensure that the results of this survey can be compared with national datasets.

The aquatic invertebrate fauna of 7 ponds on Tailend Moss was investigated. Samples of the aquatic invertebrates were collected using standard hand-net sampling methods developed for the National Pond Survey (Pond Action, 1998). A standard pond net (0.25 x 0.25 m with a 1 mm mesh) was repeatedly swept through disturbed sediment and submerged vegetation to dislodge any animals there. All the main mesohabitats in the pond were sampled so that as many invertebrate species were collected from the site as possible. Examples of typical mesohabitats are: stands of *Carex* (sedge); gravel- or muddy-bottomed shallows; areas overhung by willows, including water-bound tree-roots; stands of *Elodea*, or other submerged aquatics; flooded marginal grasses; and inflow areas. As a rough guide, the average pond might contain 3-8 mesohabitats, depending on its size and complexity. The 3 minute sampling time was therefore divided equally between the number of mesohabitats recorded: e.g. for six mesohabitats, each was sampled for 30 seconds. Where a mesohabitat was extensive or covered several widely-separated areas of the pond, the sampling time allotted to that mesohabitat was further divided in order to represent it adequately (e.g. into 6 x 5 second sub-samples). Each mesohabitat was netted vigorously to collect macroinvertebrates. Stony or sandy substrates were lightly 'kick-sampled' to disturb and capture macroinvertebrate inhabitants. Deep accumulations of soft sediment were avoided, since these areas typically support few species and collecting large amounts of mud makes later sorting extremely difficult. Similarly, large accumulations of plant material, root masses, and the like were not sampled.

A further minute was spent searching for animals that may otherwise be missed in the 3 minute sample. Areas which were searched included the water surface (for whirligig beetles, pond skaters, etc.) and under stones and logs (for limpets, snails, leeches, flatworms etc.). Additional species found were added to the main 3 minute sample. The resulting sample of invertebrates, mixed with plant material, mineral particles and detritus was placed in a large white tray and sorted on the bankside. Representative specimens were extracted and fixed with 99 % Isopropyl Alcohol.

Identification to family, species or group was undertaken by close examination under stereo or high power microscopes with reference to taxonomic books and keys. The precisions in Table 1 were used as a guide; however in some cases it was impossible to identify damaged or immature specimens.

Common Name	**Scientific Name**	**Precision**
Mussels	Bivalvia[1]	Species
Beetles (adults)	Coleoptera	Species
Beetles (larvae)	Coleoptera	Family
Crustaceans	Crustacea (Malacostraca)	Species
True-flies	Diptera	Family
Mayflies	Ephemeroptera	Species
Snails	Gastropoda	Species
True-bugs	Hemiptera	Species
Leeches	Hirudinea	Species
Moths	Lepidoptera	Species
Alderflies (incl. spongeflies)	Megaloptera	Species
Dragonflies and Damselflies	Odonata	Species
Worms	Oligochaeta	Order
Stoneflies	Plecoptera	Species
Caddisflies	Trichoptera	Species
Flatworms	Tricladida	Species

[1]Including *Sphaerium* spp. but excluding *Pisidium* spp.

Table 1 – Taxonomic precisions used in this survey

A total of 36 species were recorded during this study (appendix 1), with aquatic insects represented by seven orders.

The aquatic **Coleoptera (water beetles)** were most numerous with 12 species present including the large diving beetles *Dytiscus marginalis* and *D. semisulcatus* in ponds B and H respectively. Pond H returned the most species of water beetle with 6 species recorded. *Hydroporus palustris* was the most common species, occurring in five ponds. No water beetles were found in Pond F.

Hemiptera (true-bugs) were also well represented with seven species recorded. Pond skaters (*Gerris* sp.) and Backswimmers (*Notonecta* sp.) were recorded from six ponds. Three genera of water boatmen were recorded: *Callicorixa* from ponds E, F and I; *Hesperocorixa* from ponds E, F and H; and *Corixa* from pond D. Of particular interest was a specimen of *Hesperocorixa moesta* from pond F. This water boatmen species was recorded from Ponds F and I during surveys in 1983, at that time it appears to have been the first record of this species from Scotland. The re-discovery of it in Pond F during these surveys confirms that this species continues to occur at this site.

Five species of **Odonata (Dragonflies and damselflies)** were recorded during these surveys, with Pond E having all five species present. The Emerald damselfly (*Lestes sponsa*) was present in five of the seven ponds. Ponds A and H had no Odonata species present.

Only three species of **Trichoptera (Caddisflies)** were recorded. It is likely that more species may be present in the ponds however at the time of this study they may have either been too small to find in the samples or they may have been in their adult stage. Whilst not caddisflies, the aquatic caterpillars of a **China-mark moth** were recorded in Pond D.

Other insects orders recorded were the **Ephemeroptera** with Pond olive mayflies (*Cloeon dipterum*) recorded from all ponds apart from Ponds F and H, and **Megaloptera** with the alderfly *Sialis lutaria* which was recorded from Pond A.

Diptera (True flies) were not identified to species however the families Chironomidae (non-biting midges) and Chaoboridae (phantom midges) were found in most ponds. The main exception to this was Pond H where neither of these families was recorded.

Of the other invertebrate groups recorded during this study the **aquatic Molluscs** contained the most species with four species being found across five ponds. The most widespread species was *Physa fontinalis* which was present in Ponds A, B and D. The site also had two species from the family Lymnaeidae (*Stagnicola palustris* and *Radix balthica*) and the small White ramshorn snail (*Gyraulus albus*).

Other invertebrate species recorded during this study include the **Freshwater shrimp** *Gammarus lacustris* from Pond D, the **Freshwater leech** *Helobdella stagnalis* from Pond A; and the **Water hog-louse** (*Asellus aquaticus*) from all ponds apart from Ponds F and H.

Water mites (Hydracarina), **Seed shrimps (Ostracoda)** and **Water fleas (Cladocera)** were also found during the surveys.

A comparison of the invertebrate orders found in the ponds (Table 2) shows that in most cases the ponds have the same the composition of invertebrate orders as found in 1983 however the species composition is quite different. Of particular interest is the presence of Phantom midges (*Chaoborus* sp.) in all ponds apart from Pond H. Sticklebacks were found in ponds A, B, D and I during the original 1983 survey: however the presence of *Chaoborus* in these ponds in 2013 indicates that these ponds are now free of fish.

	Pond A		**Pond B**		**Pond D**		**Pond E**		**Pond F**		**Pond H**		**Pond I**	
Order	1983	2013	1983	2013	1983	2013	1983	2013	1983	2013	1983	2013	1983	2013
Amphipoda	•		•		•	•								
Cladocera	•	•	•	•	•	•		•						
Coleoptera	•	•	•	•	•	•	•	•	•		•	•	•	•
Diptera	•	•	•	•	•	•	•	•	•	•	•		•	•
Ephemeroptera	•	•	•	•	•	•		•						•
Hemiptera	•	•	•	•	•	•	•	•	•	•	•	•	•	•
Hirudinea		•			•									
Hydracarina	•	•		•		•							•	
Isopoda		•		•		•		•						•
Megaloptera		•	•											
Mollusca	•	•	•	•	•	•	•	•					•	•
Odonata			•	•	•	•	•	•		•	•		•	•
Oligochaeta			•											•
Ostracoda			•			•								
Pisces	•		•		•								•	
Trichoptera	•		•	•	•	•		•	•				•	•
Grand Total	10	10	13	10	11	12	5	9	4	3	4	2	8	9

Table 2 - Comparison of orders found in 1983 and 2013

The results of the current survey was compared with those of the previous surveys using a combination of measures of Species Richness and a Species Rarity Index (Biggs, et al., 2000).

To measure Species Richness (SR) the total number of species recorded from each pond was calculated. The Species Rarity Index (SRI) was calculated by allocating a numerical rarity score to each species (Table 3). The SRI is calculated by adding the individual Species Rarity Scores (SRS) together and then dividing by the Species Richness of the pond to find the average rarity value for the species present.

$$SRI = \frac{\Sigma SRS}{SR}$$

The resultant scores are then categorised according to the criteria listed in Table 4.

Status*	**Score**	**Distribution**
Common	1	Species generally regarded as common
Local[1]	2	Species either (a) confined to limited geographical area, or (b) of widespread distribution but relatively low population levels
Nationally scarce	4	Recorded from 16-100 10 x 10 km grid squares in Britain.
RDB3[2]	8	Red Data Book: Category 3 (Rare).
RDB2[2]	16	Red Data Book: Category 2 (Vulnerable).
RDB1[2]	32	Red Data Book: Category 1 (Endangered).

[1]Local: recorded from between 101 and 700 10 x 10 km grid squares in Britain;
[2]RDB: listed in the UK Red Data Books. NB The status of invertebrate species in Britain is currently under revision to bring them in line with the IUCN system. This may mean that the rarity value of some species may change

Table 3. Invertebrate Species Rarity Scores

Low	Pond supports few invertebrate species (0-10) and/or Species Rarity Score = 1.00. No local, Nationally Scarce or Red Data Book species present.
Moderate	Pond supports below average number of invertebrate species (11-30 species) and/or Species Rarity Score = 1.01 - 1.24.
High	Pond supports above average number of invertebrate species (31-50 species) and/or Species Rarity Index = 1.25-1.49.
Very High	Supports one or more Red Data Book species and/or an exceptionally rich invertebrate assemblage (50 species) and/or Species Rarity Score = 1.50 or above.

Table 4. Categories for assessing conservation value of ponds (based on a single season, 3 minute pond-net sample).

The results of this analysis show that the SRI for three ponds increased between 1983 and 2013 – Pond D from 1.20 to 1.23; Pond F from 1.75 to 1.80; and Pond H from 1.00 to 1.14. Despite these increases there has either been no change or a decrease in conservation value in the majority of ponds. Pond H was the only pond that increased its conservation value, from Low to Moderate.

The reasons for this loss of conservation value are unclear however the loss of less common species such as *Ilybius fuliginosus*, *Microvelia pygmaea* and *Valvata macrostoma*, coupled with the loss of Sticklebacks from all ponds points to a catastrophic event occurring on site. It is unlikely that a pollution event would affect Sticklebacks in all the ponds therefore the most likely reason for their loss is drying out the ponds during long periods of warm weather. This theory is backed up by evidence of a recent drop of around 30 centimetres in the water level of pond F suggesting that the water level in these ponds can vary dramatically.

	Species Richness		Species Rarity Index		Conservation Value	
	1983	**2013**	**1983**	**2013**	**1983**	**2013**
Pond A	13	7	2.23	1.14	Very High	Moderate
Pond B	12	12	1.42	1.17	High	Moderate
Pond D	15	13	1.20	1.23	Moderate	Moderate
Pond E	9	13	1.22	1.08	Moderate	Moderate
Pond F	4	5	1.75	1.80	Very High	Very High
Pond H	5	7	1.00	1.14	Low	Moderate
Pond I	6	13	1.50	1.31	Very High	High

Table 5. Species Richness, Species Rarity Index and Conservation Value for ponds at Tailend Moss.

References

Biggs, J., Williams, P., Whitfield, M., Fox, G. and Nicolet, P. 2000. *Ponds, pools and lochans: guidance on good practice in the management and creation of small water bodies in Scotland.* Scottish Environment Protection Agency, Stirling.

Pond Action 1998. *A Guide to the Methods of the National Pond Survey*. Pond Action, Oxford.

Richardson, B.A. and Shiells, B.M. 1984. Pond ecology – Tailend Moss Nature Reserve, West Lothian. *Forth Naturalist and Historian* **8**, 25-40.

Acknowledgements

The author would like to thank the Scottish Wildlife Trust for access to their Tailend Moss reserve.

Appendix 1 – Distribution of species in the seven ponds

	Pond A	Pond B	Pond D	Pond E	Pond F	Pond H	Pond I
Aeshna juncea				•	•		•
Agabus bipustulatus						•	•
Asellus aquaticus	•	•	•	•			•
Callicorixa praeusta				•	•		•
Chaoboridae	•	•	•	•	•		•
Chironomidae	•	•	•	•	•		
Cladocera	•	•	•	•			
Cloeon dipterum	•	•	•	•			•
Coenagrioniidae			•				
Colymbetes fuscus						•	
Corixa panzeri			•				
Corixidae		•			•		
Dytiscus marginalis		•					
Dytiscus semisulcatus						•	

	Pond A	Pond B	Pond D	Pond E	Pond F	Pond H	Pond I
Enallagma cyathigerum		•	•	•			
Gammarus lacustris			•				
Gerris lacustris			•				
Gerris sp.	•	•		•	•	•	
Gyraulus albus		•					
Gyrinidae							•
Gyrinus sp.							•
Gyrinus substriatus				•			
Helobdella stagnalis	•						
Helophilus pendulus			•				
Hesperocorixa moesta					•		
Hesperocorixa sahlbergi				•		•	
Holocentropus picicornis		•					
Hydracarina	•	•	•				
Hydroporus gyllenhalii						•	
Hydroporus palustris	•	•	•			•	•
Hydroporus planus						•	
Hygrotus inaequalis			•				•
Hyphydrus ovatus		•					
Ilybius aenescens							•
Lestes sponsa		•	•	•	•		•
Limnephilus sp.			•				
Nepa cinerea							•
Notonecta glauca			•	•	•		•
Notonecta sp.	•	•					
Nymphylidae sp.			•				
Ostracoda			•				
Phryganea bipunctata				•			
Phryganea sp.							•
Physa fontinalis	•	•	•				
Physa sp.	•	•					
Pyrrhosoma nymphula		•		•			
Radix balthica				•			
Rhantus exsoletus	•	•					
Sialis lutaria	•						
Stagnicola palustris			•				•
Sympetrum danae				•	•		•
Triaenodes bicolor			•				
Velia sp.	•						

A SURVEY OF THE HOVERFLIES OF THE INNER FORTH

Scott Shanks

Hoverflies (Syrphidae) are among our most charismatic invertebrates, and recording these often colourful flies has become very popular in recent years. The UK's 281 species display a diversity of lifestyles and favoured habitats making them an excellent indicator group.

In 1981, a checklist of 106 hoverfly species occurring in the 10 km squares NS89 and NS99 (Clackmannanshire and East Stirlingshire) was published by MacGowan (1981). The data for that study had been collected from a variety of sites during 1978-1981. The current study, undertaken as part of the FNH 'What's Changed' project 2013, presents a resurvey of the hoverfly fauna within these 10 km squares some 30 years after the original survey.

During the 2013 survey, eight sites in the 10 km squares NS89 and NS99, and some from 1 km square NS7993 were visited with volunteers to record hoverflies (Figure 1). These included some of the sites previously visited by MacGowan. Recent (2011, 2012) hoverfly records from the University of Stirling campus were also included in this study (Figure 1).

A variety of habitats were visited within each site, with recording effort focused on sunny, flower-rich areas to look for nectar-feeding and basking adult hoverflies. An aerial net was used to collect active adult hoverflies around

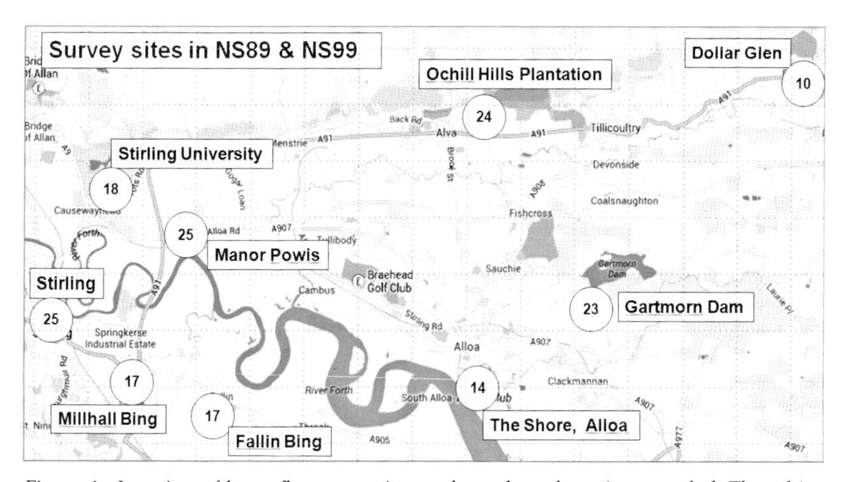

Figure 1. Location of hoverfly survey sites and number of species recorded. The white circles show the number of hoverfly species recorded at that site during the current survey.

flowers, and a sweep net and pooter were used to collect individuals resting in long grass and vegetation. Species that could be identified in the field were recorded and released. Other specimens were retained for identification using a microscope. Where possible, specimens were identified to species level, however the females of some genera can only be identified to genus.

Records of other invertebrates were also noted on each site visit. Two volunteers received training in the identification of hoverflies and helped identify specimens collected during some of the surveys.

During the 2013 survey, records of 64 hoverfly species were collected from the nine sites: 54 species in NS89 and 35 species in NS99 (Figure 2). Forty-eight species that had previously been recorded by MacGowan (1981) were not recorded in the current survey and have had no NS89 or NS99 records in the last 20 years. Six previously unrecorded species were identified as new to these squares including *Chrysotoxum bicinctum, Eriozona syrphoides, Ferdinandea cuprea, Pipiza bimaculata, Platycheirus ramsarensis* and *Sphaerophoria scripta.*

Analysis of the Hoverfly Recording Scheme data available from the National Biodiversity Network (NBN) database revealed that 40 species of hoverflies had been recorded in NS89 and NS99 up to 2012. This dataset does not contain the records from MacGowan's orginal survey (1981). The only species listed in the Hoverfly Recording Scheme dataset that was not recorded in the current survey or in MacGowan's 1981survey was *Cheilosia vulpina* which was recorded in Stirlingshire in 1983, but has a predominantly southern distribution and this appears to be the only Scottish record (Morris and Ball 2013; Stubbs and Falk 2002).

Of the 106 hoverfly species listed by MacGowan (1981), 29 species (27 %) have not been recorded since 1981, and 48 species (45 %) have not been recorded since 1992. The absent species are generally rare or uncommon in Scotland with a decreasing UK trend in recent years (Morris and Ball 2013), suggesting that they may have been lost due to habitat loss or other environmental changes (Figure 3).

263 hoverfly records were collected during the survey and will be uploaded to the NBN. Records of other invertebrates (Coleoptera, Diptera (non-Syrphidae), Lepidoptera, Orthoptera, Odonata, Hymenoptera and Hemiptera) were also collected during the hoverfly surveys and will be uploaded to NBN along with the hoverfly data.

New hoverfly species in Clackmannanshire

Chrysotoxum bicinctum is a distinctive black and yellow wasp-mimic with dark brown markings on its wings. The species is associated with open grasslands and woodland rides and the larvae are thought to feed on root aphids in ants' nests. It is common and widespread in southern England, but less common further north and in Scotland. This species was not recorded by MacGowan, but he does mention that it had previously been recorded from the Aberfoyle area by A. E. J. Carter around 1910 (MacGowan 1981) (Plate 9a).

Eriozonia syrphoides is a Nationally Scarce bumblebee mimic associated with open and sunny rides in conifer plantations, where larvae are thought to feed on conifer-dwelling aphids. It is a relatively recent colonist in the UK, having first been recorded in Snowdonia in 1968 and its range expansion seems to have been facilitated by the large number of spruce plantations planted in the 1980s. This species was mentioned by MacGowan (1981) as having been recorded on a number of occasions in the Carron Valley since the early 1970s, but was not on his checklist.

Ferdinandea cuprea is a woodland specialist with a distinctively grey-striped thorax and brassy abdomen. The larvae feed on yeasts and other microbes in sap runs on trees. Suitable sap runs can be fairly infrequent even in large woodlands, and so while this species is widespread across the UK it is rarely found in large numbers (Plate 9b).

Pipiza bimaculata was recorded in the grounds of Stirling University. This genus has a number of very similar species, which are generally either all black, or black with a pair of orange-yellow spots on the abdomen. *P. bimaculata* is thought to be widespread, although possibly under-recorded due to difficulties with identification. It can generally be identified by its small size, dark tarsi and clear wings compared to the more common and widespread *Pipiza noctiluca,* which on average is bigger, with some yellow on its tarsi and a dark wing-cloud. The larvae are thought to feed on leaf-rolling aphids. Due to difficulties with identification, this specimen is awaiting further verification.

Platycheirus ramsarensis is a small dark narrow-bodied hoverfly with yellow markings similar to the more widespread *P. clypeatus.* This northern species is associated with moorlands, uplands and raised bogs. The larvae of this genus are thought to feed on ground-layer aphids in leaf litter or wetland vegetation.

Sphaerophoria scripta is an elongated, narrow-bodied grassland hoverfly. Male *Sphaerophoria* have a large genital capsule under the end of the abdomen. This species generally has yellow bands across the abdomen and a distinctively long body compared to its wings. The species is common and widespread in southern England, but is less common further north. It is thought that Scottish records may be of migrants from southern populations. The larvae are thought to feed on ground-layer dwelling aphids.

Recording hoverflies

Anyone interested in finding out more about recording hoverflies would be advised to obtain a copy, of either *British Hoverflies* by Stubbs & Falk (ISBN:

1-899935-0503) or *Britain's Hoverflies: An introduction to the hoverflies of Britain* by Ball and Morris (ISBN: 978-0-691-15659-0). Another useful resource for recorders is Steven Falk's online 'Flickr' gallery of hoverfly photographs, that shows key identifying features on both live and pinned specimens. https://www.flickr.com/photos/63075200@N07/collections/

References

MacGowan, I. 1981. Hoverflies of the Stirling Area. *Forth Naturalist and Historian* 6, 63-75.

Morris, R. and Ball, S. 2013. *Britain's Hoverflies: An introduction to the hoverflies of Britain*. Wildguides.

Stubbs, A. and Falk, S.J. 2002. *British Hoverflies*. The Dorset Press (2nd Edition).

Acknowledgements

The author would like to thank the following volunteers who helped survey sites, provided their records and/or helped with specimen identification: Stuart Bence, Lorna Blackmore, Rebecca Cairns, Michael Christie, Noelia Collado Salas, Niall Currie, Leanne Hunter, Mike Hunter, Angela Lloyd, David Pryce, Melissa Shaw and Alison Smith.

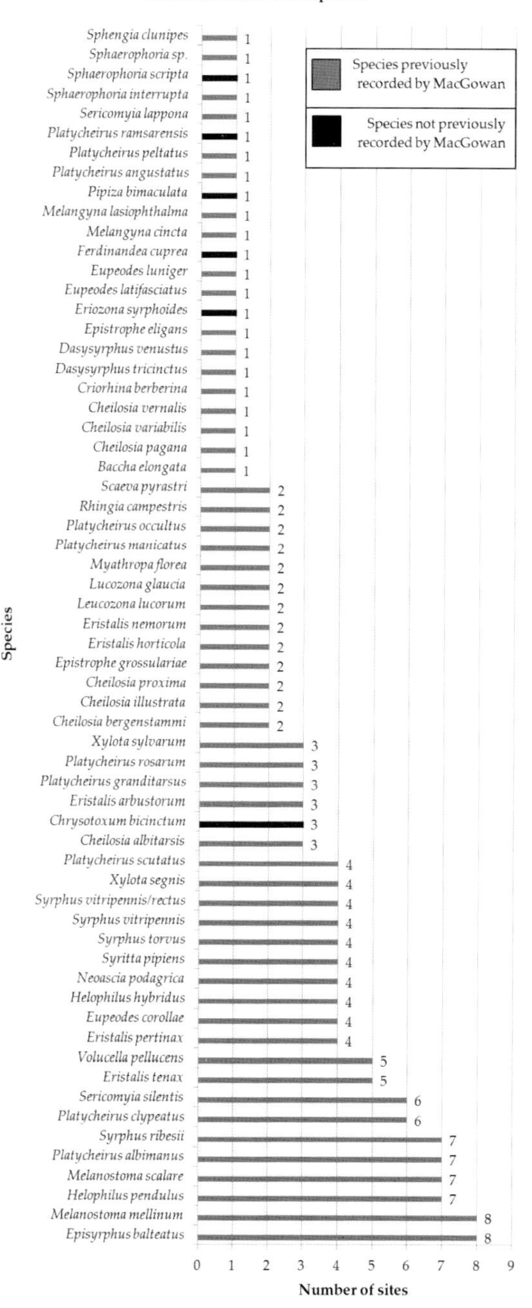

Figure 2.
List of hoverfly species recorded during current survey and number of sites they were recorded at. Species with grey bars were previously reported by MacGowan (1981). The black bars indicate species newly recorded in NS89 and NS90 during the current survey.

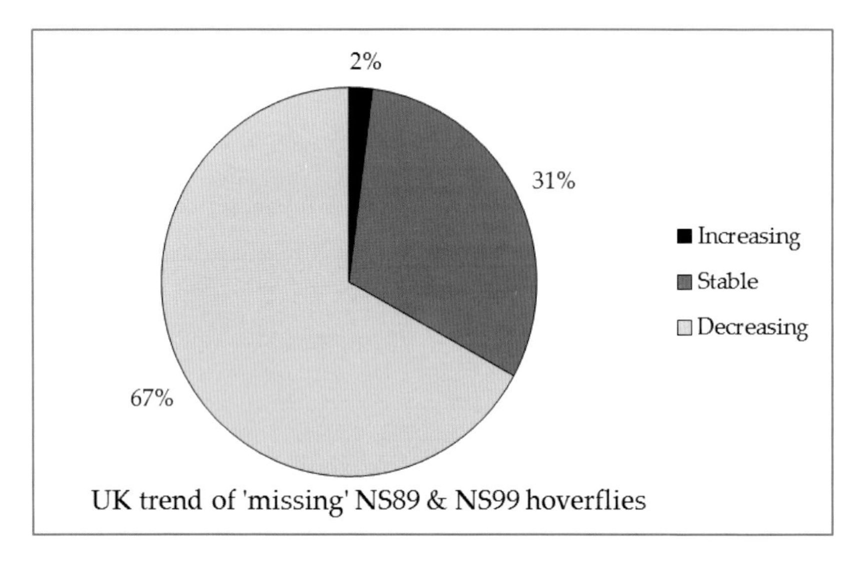

Figure 3. Forty-eight species of hoverflies initially reported by MacGowan (1981) were not re-recorded in the current survey. The majority of these are rare or uncommon in Scotland (Morris & Ball, 2013).

FALKIRK MOTHS

Heather Young

As part of the 2013 '*What's Changed?*' project, light-trapping at night to record moths was carried out in three locations in the Falkirk area to compare current moth fauna with the list published in the *Forth Naturalist and Historian*, volume 7 by C.W.N. Holmes (Holmes, 1982/3). This list comprised a collation of Holmes' records from "twenty or so" years of light trapping and field recording making direct comparison impossible over such a short time period, so an additional examination was carried out of recent records from the databases for the two vice counties sharing parts of the Falkirk district (Stirlingshire (VC86) and West Lothian (VC84)).

Light trapping was carried out at the Scottish Wildlife Trust reserves of Carron Glen, Fankerton (NS785835; seven trapping events), Carron Dam, Stenhousemuir (NS875826; three trapping events), and Bo'mains Meadow, Bo'ness (NS988794; two trapping events). Carron Glen is a stretch of ancient deciduous woodland along a steep-sided gorge of the River Carron, just west of Denny. It lies within a 10 kilometre square (NS78) that until 2013 had only 25 moth records in the National Moth Recording Scheme database, and was therefore a priority for generating new data to be added to the National Biodiversity Network. Carron Dam is the site of a partially-drained reservoir originally used to supply water to the Carron Iron Works, and is now one of the largest wetlands in the Falkirk area, with a range of fen and woodland habitats. It is only around 2.5 kilometres from the North Bantaskine site that generated many of Holmes' records in his 1982/3 list, and could explain the presence of several wetland specialist species in his garden, such as bulrush wainscot (*Nonagria typhae*). Bo'mains Meadow is a small wildflower meadow just south of Bo'ness best known for its colony of greater butterfly orchid.

Holmes considered his recording of macro-moths and Hepialidae (swift moths) to have been comprehensive, but not so for that of micro-moths and day-flying species, so no comparisons will be made for those families. Five species of macro-moth not recorded by Holmes were found during light trapping for the project; welsh wave (*Venusia cambrica*), early tooth-striped (*Trichopteryx carpinata*), slender brindle (*Apamea scolopacina*) (Plate 7a), Lempke's gold spot (*Plusia putnami*) (Plate 7b), and marsh oblique-barred (*Hypenodes humidalis*). A further six species had been recorded in the Falkirk area in 2012 or 2013 that were not mentioned in Holmes' list; orange swift (*Hepialus sylvina*), spruce carpet (*Thera britannica*), grey arches (*Polia nebulosa*), pale pinion (*Lithophane hepatica*), early grey (*Xylocampa areola*), and straw dot (*Rivula sericealis*). Most of these were present in Stirlingshire or West Lothian while Holmes was recording. Some are regarded as 'local' – the national status allotted by the JNCC to a species recorded from 101 – 300 10 km squares in

Great Britain since January 1st 1960; marsh oblique-barred is a Nationally Scarce B species – recorded from 31 – 100 10 km squares; others have previously shown a more western distribution and may be expanding their ranges eastwards, for example, grey arches. Lempke's gold spot was only described as a separate species to gold spot (*Plusia festucae*) in 1966, and may have been overlooked, although gold spot itself was described by Holmes as not common. Two species are relatively recent arrivals; slender brindle was first recorded in Stirlingshire in 2005, while pale pinion first appeared in West Lothian in 2008. Both are considered to be expanding their range northwards through Scotland (Knowler, 2010), possibly aided by climate change.

It is impossible to say that any species recorded by Holmes is no longer present in the Falkirk area, but one that he regularly recorded has not been seen since 1996, and may have become extinct – the v-moth (*Macaria wauaria*). This moth showed a 99 % population decrease in the Rothamsted light-trap network over the period 1968-2007, much of this since 1996. The larvae feed on currants and gooseberries, and the most likely causes of its decline are reduced cultivation of soft fruits and increased use of insecticides (Fox et al, 2013).

During trapping for the project at Carron Dam reserve in Stenhousemuir, two species of micro-moth were found that had not previously been recorded in Stirlingshire, both specialist wetland species, and both with only a handful of historical records in Scotland. Small china-mark (*Cataclysta lemnata*) (Plate 8a), a crambid moth with an aquatic larva that constructs a protective case and feeds on duckweeds (Plate 8b), has been recorded at only three other Scottish sites. *Phalonidia manniana*, a tiny tortrix moth with a larva that mines the stems of gypsywort and water mint, also has only three previous records in Scotland (M. Young, pers. comm.).

In general, it would seem that as far as macro-moths are concerned, '*What's changed?*' has mostly been positive over the course of the last 30 years, with several new species having moved in, and several described as rare by Holmes in 1982 now are regarded as common (Knowler, 2010).

The appended list contains only those moths recorded during light-trapping for the project, and is not a comprehensive inventory of species present in the Falkirk area.

Acknowledgements

Thanks are due to the Scottish Wildlife Trust and the volunteers who assisted in the light-trapping for the project: Roy Sexton, Tony Rogers, Craig Macadam, Rosemary Young, Yasmine Horrill, and Lorraine Hughes. I am grateful to John Knowler and Mark Cubitt (moth recorders for VC 86 (Stirlingshire) and VC 84 (West Lothian) respectively) for the provision of historical information on the macro-moths, and Ian Edwards and Ian King for additional 2012-13 records. I am also indebted to Mark Young for assistance with the identification of some of the micro-moths, and information on their status in Scotland.

References

Fox, R., Parsons, M.S., Chapman, J.W. *et al.* (2013). *The State of Britain's Larger Moths 2013.* Butterfly Conservation and Rothamsted Research, Wareham, Dorset.

Holmes, C.W.N. (1982/83). Lepidoptera of the Falkirk District of Central Region. *Forth Naturalist and Historian,* **7**, 57-76.

Knowler, J.T. (2010). *An Annotated Checklist of the Larger Moths of Stirlingshire, West Perthshire and Dunbartonshire.* Glasgow Natural History Society, Glasgow.

Species List

Hepialus humuli	Ghost Moth	(Linnaeus, 1758)
Hepialus fusconebulosa	Map-winged Swift	(DeGeer, 1778)
Anthophila fabriciana		(Linnaeus, 1767)
Argyresthia goedartella		(Linnaeus, 1758)
Yponomeuta evonymella	Bird-cherry Ermine	(Linnaeus, 1758)
Phalonidia manniana		(Fischer von Roslerstamm, 1839)
Cnephasia asseclana	Flax Tortrix	(Denis & Schiffermüller, 1775)
Acleris laterana		(Fabricius, 1794)
Acleris emargana		(Fabricius, 1775)
Apotomis betuletana		(Haworth, 1811)
Agriphila straminella		(Denis & Schiffermüller, 1775)
Agriphila tristella		(Denis & Schiffermüller, 1775)
Dipleurina lacustrata		(Panzer, 1804)
Elophila nymphaeata	Brown China-mark	(Linnaeus, 1758)
Cataclysta lemnata	Small China-mark	(Linnaeus, 1758)
Udea lutealis		(Hübner, 1809)
Pleuroptya ruralis	Mother of Pearl	(Scopoli, 1763)
Poecilocampa populi	December Moth	(Linnaeus, 1758)
Geometra papilionaria	Large Emerald	(Linnaeus, 1758)
Idaea biselata	Small Fan-footed Wave	(Hufnagel, 1767)
Idaea aversata	Riband Wave	(Linnaeus, 1758)
Xanthorhoe designata	Flame Carpet	(Hufnagel, 1767)
Scotopteryx chenopodiata	Shaded Broad-bar	(Linnaeus, 1758)
Ecliptopera silaceata	Small Phoenix	(Denis & Schiffermüller, 1775)
Chloroclysta siterata	Red-green Carpet	(Hufnagel, 1767)
Chloroclysta citrata	Dark Marbled Carpet	(Linnaeus, 1761)
Chloroclysta truncata	Common Marbled Carpet	(Hufnagel, 1767)
Hydriomena furcata	July Highflyer	(Thunberg, 1784)
Epirrita dilutata agg.	November Moth agg.	(Unknown)
Operophtera brumata	Winter Moth	(Linnaeus, 1758)
Perizoma didymata	Twin-spot Carpet	(Linnaeus, 1758)
Eupithecia abbreviata	Brindled Pug	(Stephens, 1831)
Pasiphila rectangulata	Green Pug	(Linnaeus, 1758)
Venusia cambrica	Welsh Wave	(Curtis, 1839)
Trichopteryx carpinata	Early Tooth-striped	(Borkhausen, 1794)
Lomaspilis marginata	Clouded Border	(Linnaeus, 1758)
Chiasmia clathrata	Latticed Heath	(Linnaeus, 1758)
Opisthograptis luteolata	Brimstone Moth	(Linnaeus, 1758)
Crocallis elinguaria	Scalloped Oak	(Linnaeus, 1758)
Colotois pennaria	Feathered Thorn	(Linnaeus, 1761)

Agriopis aurantiaria	Scarce Umber	(Hübner, 1799)
Erannis defoliaria	Mottled Umber	(Clerck, 1759)
Peribatodes rhomboidaria	Willow Beauty	(Denis & Schiffermüller, 1775)
Alcis repandata	Mottled Beauty	(Linnaeus, 1758)
Ectropis bistortata	Engrailed	(Goeze, 1781)
Hylaea fasciaria	Barred Red	(Linnaeus, 1758)
Ptilodon capucina	Coxcomb Prominent	(Linnaeus, 1758)
Arctia caja	Garden Tiger	(Linnaeus, 1758)
Spilosoma lubricipeda	White Ermine	(Linnaeus, 1758)
Ochropleura plecta	Flame Shoulder	(Linnaeus, 1761)
Noctua pronuba	Large Yellow Underwing	(Linnaeus, 1758)
Noctua comes	Lesser Yellow Underwing	(Hübner, 1813)
Noctua janthe	Lesser Broad-bordered Yellow Underwing	(Borkhausen, 1792)
Eugnorisma glareosa	Autumnal Rustic	(Esper, 1788)
Diarsia dahlii	Barred Chestnut	(Hübner, 1813)
Diarsia brunnea	Purple Clay	(Denis & Schiffermüller, 1775)
Diarsia rubi	Small Square-spot	(Vieweg, 1790)
Xestia triangulum	Double Square-spot	(Hufnagel, 1766)
Xestia baja	Dotted Clay	(Denis & Schiffermüller, 1775)
Xestia sexstrigata	Six-striped Rustic	(Haworth, 1809)
Xestia xanthographa	Square-spot Rustic	(Denis & Schiffermüller, 1775)
Naenia typica	Gothic	(Linnaeus, 1758)
Lacanobia oleracea	Bright-line Brown-eye	(Linnaeus, 1758)
Melanchra pisi	Broom Moth	(Linnaeus, 1758)
Cerapteryx graminis	Antler Moth	(Linnaeus, 1758)
Orthosia cruda	Small Quaker	(Denis & Schiffermüller, 1775)
Orthosia cerasi	Common Quaker	(Fabricius, 1775)
Orthosia gothica	Hebrew Character	(Linnaeus, 1758)
Mythimna impura	Smoky Wainscot	(Hübner, 1808)
Xanthia togata	Pink-barred Sallow	(Esper, 1788)
Phlogophora meticulosa	Angle Shades	(Linnaeus, 1758)
Cosmia trapezina	Dun-bar	(Linnaeus, 1758)
Apamea monoglypha	Dark Arches	(Hufnagel, 1766)
Apamea crenata	Clouded-bordered Brindle	(Hufnagel, 1766)
Apamea remissa	Dusky Brocade	(Hübner, 1809)
Apamea sordens	Rustic Shoulder-knot	(Hufnagel, 1766)
Apamea scolopacina	Slender Brindle	(Esper, 1788)
Oligia strigilis agg.	Marbled Minor agg.	(Unknown)
Mesapamea secalis agg.	Common Rustic agg.	(Unknown)
Chortodes pygmina	Small Wainscot	(Haworth, 1809)
Hydraecia micacea	Rosy Rustic	(Esper, 1789)
Celaena haworthii	Haworth's Minor	(Curtis, 1829)
Celaena leucostigma	Crescent	(Hübner, 1808)
Nonagria typhae	Bulrush Wainscot	(Thunberg, 1784)
Hoplodrina sp.	Hoplodrina species	(Unknown)
Plusia putnami	Lempke's Gold Spot	(Lempke, 1966)
Autographa gamma	Silver Y	(Linnaeus, 1758)
Autographa pulchrina	Beautiful Golden Y	(Haworth, 1809)
Hypena proboscidalis	Snout	(Linnaeus, 1758)
Hypenodes humidalis	Marsh Oblique-barred	(Doubleday, 1850)
Zanclognatha tarsipennalis	Fan-foot	(Treitschke, 1835)
Herminia grisealis	Small Fan-foot	(Denis & Schiffermüller, 1775)

A SURVEY OF LARGE HEATH, PURPLE HAIRSTREAK AND NORTHERN BROWN ARGUS BUTTERFLY POPULATIONS IN THE FORTH VALLEY

Stuart Bence and Lorna M. Blackmore

Contributors: Ryan Blackmore, Michael Christie, Joanne Gibb, John Oates, William Purdie, Melissa Shaw, Roy Sexton, Steven Wilkinson.

To celebrate 2013 The Year of Natural Scotland the Forth Naturalist and Historian was awarded a grant by Scottish Natural Heritage SNH to revisit some of the early wildlife and habitat surveys published in the FNH Journal 30 years ago.

This account concerns a project led by us on behalf of the Stirling University Nature Society who supplied most of the undergraduate volunteers. It was based on George Thomson's (1976) account *Our Disappearing Butterflies* which appeared in the first volume of the Journal and the proposal was to update some of his observations. Of course it was not possible to survey all the 45 species of butterfly referred to in Thomson's paper and after preliminary discussions with Paul Kirkland and Scott Shanks of Butterfly Conservation we agreed to concentrate our efforts on establishing the extent of the Forth Valley populations of large heath, purple hairstreak and northern brown argus. Butterfly surveys are dependent on sunshine and we were fortunate in having ideal conditions during much of survey period from May – September 2013.

Large Heath

The preferred habitat of large heath butterfly *Coenonympha tullia* (Plate 11a) is lowland raised bogs. A peatland specialist, it lays its eggs on hare's-tail cotton-grass *Eriophorum vaginatum* which is the main food plant of the caterpillar. After overwintering in tussocks of cotton grass the caterpillars pupate in May followed by the emergence of adults in mid-June which then fly until late July. Our surveys, which were completed in this flight period, revealed that the adults were always associated with sites that contained their main caterpillar food plant, hare's-tail cotton-grass, as well as the adults' main nectaring plant cross-leaved heath *Erica tetralix*. While the presence of these food plants is essential to sustain the life cycle of the large heath there are many locations where the plants were found without the butterflies. Often this is due to previous disturbance of the bog causing the loss of the species.

In Scotland there are two forms of large heath; a southern subspecies *polydama* which has an orange brown underside with six spots on the hind wing and the northern *scotica* which is paler with a spotless hind wing. The literature suggested that the Forth Valley should represent the boundary between these populations (Futter et al. 2006) however in our survey we only encountered the *polydama* form.

Thomson (1976) predicted that there would be a local decline in this species due to the drainage and afforestation of raised bogs which was occurring on a major scale at the time he wrote his account. Drainage leads to drying of the bog which in turn encourages the growth of trees such as birch *Betula spp* and Scot's pine *Pinus sylvestris* which exacerbate the problem. Food plants are reduced under these conditions and heather or ling (*Calluna vulgaris*) can come to dominate the habitat. Thomson's prediction was subsequently borne out by national data in the Millennium Atlas of Butterflies in Britain and Ireland (Asher et al., 2001) which showed that this butterfly had been lost from 47 % of the 10 km recording squares. As a result large heath was designated as a species of Conservation Concern in the UK Biodiversity Action Plan and is listed on Schedule 5 of the 1981 Wildlife and Countryside Act. To try and encourage more local monitoring SNH organised a large heath training course in 2005 which reported the butterfly numbers at seven sites in the FNH Journal (Pickett and Stoneman, 2005). We have extended this programme to 26 locations spread over a much wider area from Cumbernauld in the west to Falkirk in the east. These additional sites were selected because they were: other locations for which Butterfly Conservation had large heath records; sites identified using an email survey of local butterfly recorders; potential raised and blanket bog sites identified using Google Earth and geological maps.

Figure 1 shows the distribution of the 26 peatland areas surveyed of which only 13 were found to have populations of the large heath. Table 1 shows the numbers seen during 45 min transect surveys which were always conducted in warm sunshine during the period 24th June to the 31st of July 2013. These were the same survey methods as described by Stoneman and Pickett (2005). Some of the peatland systems were very large and multiple transects were walked as indicated in Table 1. The dates of any historical records at each site are also shown.

The region which contained the greatest numbers of large heath in the Forth Valley was Flanders Moss and its surrounding satellite peatlands. The highest numbers were recorded on Shirgarton Moss 1 km north of Kippen where during 45 minutes 867 large heath were seen. There were also high counts on Killorn moss 3 km to the east. Although both these bogs had high counts in the 2005 survey the numbers had increased considerably. This is likely to be the result of recent management involving extensive damming to retain water together with the removal of trees which has aided the recovery of the food plant. Unlike Killorn, Shirgarton Moss is considered to be one of the few mosses in the area still containing an intact hydrology, potentially explaining the discrepancy between the numbers of the large heath present on these two sites.

On the 821 hectares of the main body of Flanders Moss National Nature Reserve the management regime and hence the vegetation structure varies greatly from site to site. Many of the more peripheral sites had good numbers of butterflies including Ballangrew in the west, South Flanders in the south west, Easter Poldar in the southeast and East Moss-side in the northeast. Most of these sites have been grazed and are in reasonable condition having been managed by damming drainage ditches and the manual removal of trees. This has helped to keep the bog damp preventing heather dominance over the large heath's food plants. Poldar Moss by the boardwalk at the NNR visitor centre has rather lower numbers but they are slowly increasing probably as a result of the intensive conservation work there. In the large central section of Flanders Moss the numbers found on each of the 25 transects varied greatly. Those on the east side between East Moss-side and Poldar Moss rarely had more than ten sightings. In the southern area between Poldar Moss and the south of the lochan counts were even fewer. Numbers were much higher (60-80) in an arc to the west of the lochan extending up to 250 m north of it. Across the northern moss south of the Wards of Goodie only two butterflies were seen on three transects which is consistent the Picket and Stoneman's (2005) data. This large area of peatland needs extensive management to reverse the historical damage due to ditching and tree growth. SNH has a programme of management regimes to address the issue see: http://www.snh.org.uk/pdfs/publications/nnr/The_Reserve_Plan_for_Flanders_Moss

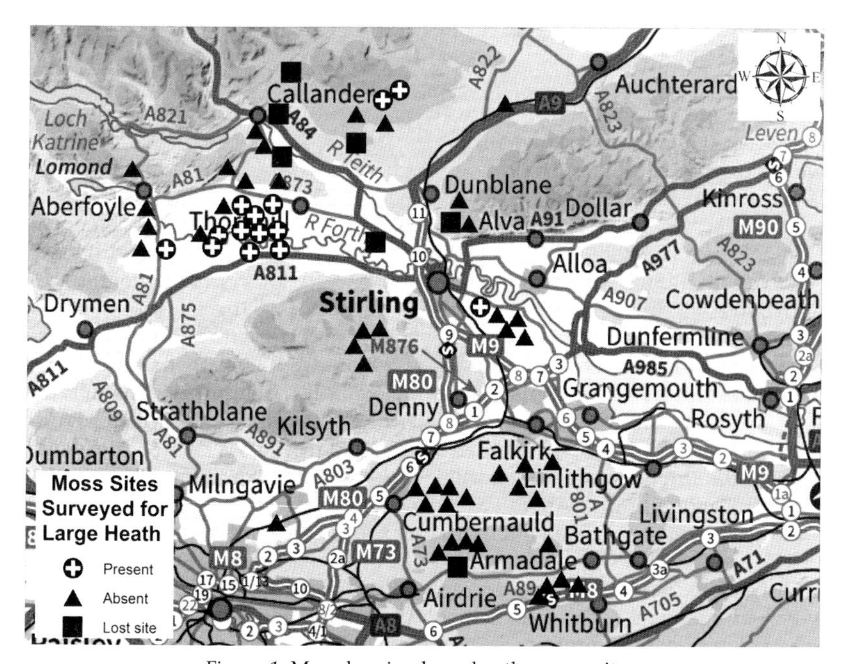

Figure 1. Map showing large heath survey sites.

Ochtertyre Moss (Figure 2) near Blairdrummond Safari Park was once part of Blairdrummond or Kincardine Moss most of which was removed by Lord Kames in the 1770s. Originally this bog must have been almost contiguous with Flanders Moss but now the two are separated by 7 km of farmland. Although there are historical records of its presence no large heath were found here either in this or the preceding 2005 survey. This moss was once forested and was partially cleared which may have led to the loss of the butterfly. Food plant availability is poor as common cotton-grass (*Eriophorum angustifolium)* is much more prolific than hare's-tail cotton-grass and the nectaring plants are also uncommon.

Figure 2 The survey team setting out through the cotton grass on Ochtertyre Moss. Photograph R.Sexton

On the un-forested remains of Western Flanders Moss (ie west of the Port of Menteith to Arnprior road) two new large heath sites were discovered at Collymoon and Whitehill bogs both with healthy numbers of butterflies. These sites had been thought to be lost perhaps because the edges of the mosses are covered in mature Scots Pine which gives the impression that the whole moss is covered in woodland. However in the centre of each moss there were still areas of peatland that have remained damp and retained cotton grass and cross-leaved heath under a sparse canopy of bog myrtle (*Myrica gale)* and mature Scots pine. Whitehill Moss had far lower counts than Collymoon possibly because the site is drier due to water loss through an eroded area where it borders with farmland. Collymoon also had more food plant species with less heather possibly due to the wetter conditions. Offerance Moss south of Kelty Water on the A81 Aberfoyle road is another surviving fragment of Western Flanders Moss with a good population of large heath, the site consists of areas that are quite damp with evidence of grazing together with competition from bog myrtle reducing heather dominance. Along the A81 from Offerance Moss to Lake of Menteith there are a number of peatland sites that have become rush dominated wet grasslands. To the south of the Lake of Menteith (NS 590 981) there are fragments of peatland similar to Collymoon but the majority of it has been drained and planted as commercial forestry so there were no large heath present.

More peatlands are to be found to the north of Flanders Moss in an area centred around Loch Rusky. No large heath sites were found here although there are historical records. The majority of these bogs have become wet grassland with the exception of a small area immediately south of Callander (NN 627 067) and another at Loch Rusky (NN 616 029) both of which have been badly damaged by drainage ditches and are a fraction of their original size.

The only raised bog site where we found large heath outside the Flanders Moss complex was Butterfly Conservation's reserve for the species at Wester Moss near Fallin. The site appears to have had low but consistent numbers since 2005 and it is to be hoped that all the recent efforts to remove trees and block drainage ditches will bear fruit in the near future. To the east of Wester Moss there are two small pockets of peatland (NS 847 907) where large heath had been reported however both have now dried out and have become covered in bracken so no longer support any peatland species. Two kilometres south east between Cowie and Airth there is a large peatland system including Easter Moss and Dunmore Moss. Easter Moss has been drained in the last few years and has had a large amount of covering vegetation removed. The neighbouring Dunmore Moss has been subjected to peat extraction historically and is now covered with a blanket of hare's-tail cotton-grass with plenty of cross-leaved heath. In spite of its proximity to Wester Moss neither we nor other recent recording parties found large heath there. Mark and recapture studies have found the adult butterflies are very sedentary and rarely move more than 100 m (Asher et al. 2001) so the population from Wester Moss is unlikely to recolonize this site. The centre of the bog has been lowered several metres as a result of peat extraction and floods in winter. This could result in the hibernating caterpillars of large heath drowning if the water level rises above the tussocks in which they reside. Letham Moss 2.5 km to the south was considered by Thomson (1978) to be the main stronghold for large heath in the area. Industrial scale peat extraction over this 175 hectare site occurred until recently and although some parts were supposed to be left intact almost all the peat has now been removed.

The largest peatland system in the area is on the Slamannan plateau an expansive area which stretches between Falkirk, Cumbernauld, Bathgate and Caldercruix. We carried out 91 transects in the region. South of Falkirk around Slamannan on Gardrum, Darnrig and surrounding mosses we found almost all the bogs had been historically drained and subject to peat removal and are now largely dominated by heather. Some sites have been reopened for modern peat extraction, which is more efficient than older methods and has left many areas with exposed waterlogged peat devoid of vegetation. Although we found no large heath there were a few small and isolated bog-remnants near Quarryhead (NS 895 759) that contained peatland moths like the emperor moth, beautiful yellow underwing and true lover's-knot.

South east of Cumbernauld around Fannyside Loch the bogs in the area had all been prepared for peat extraction or forestry in the past. Several parts have since been planted with forestry and a few were exploited for peat. None had large heath but it is worth noting that to the east there is two areas of bog (NS 819 736 and NS 824 742) which although greatly reduced in size remain good sites supporting the rare Manchester treble bar moth.

Blackridge train station (near Armadale) has two bog systems near it. The northerly one (NS 914 669) is becoming dominated by heather and trees while the southern site (NS 920 667) showed evidence of some peatland extraction and preparation work for forestry though the main area appears to have become rewetted. Again large heath were not found though other peatland moths like beautiful yellow underwing and the emperor moth still occur. To the west there are another two peatland systems (NS 898 661 and NS 898 654) but both of these have since been largely forested. To the north (NS 897 683) is another site which remains damp in the centre with vaporer and Manchester treble bar moths but unfortunately no large heath.

Next to the town of Caldercruix there are a set of bogs (NS 814 686) last known to have large heath 34 years ago but they have been drained and overgrazed since and there were no signs of the butterfly. To the north west many of the bogs have been historically mined and there was a large fire when we were surveying possibly started for red grouse heather management. To the north east the bogs are currently being subjected to peat extraction.

There were also several isolated raised bog sites where no large heath were found. Brucefield Moss west of Clackmannan was a healthy peatland 40 years ago but is now completely covered in a dense conifer plantation. By contrast Shelforkie or Carsebreck Moss near Braco is a wet and actively growing bog with few trees and plenty of cotton grass and cross-leaved heath. Annual butterfly counts by Mike Bell and the 2005 survey failed to locate any large heath, like us. It has been suggested that the site is too exposed (Picket and Stoneman, 2005) or perhaps that the butterfly was killed off in the past by heather burns when it was managed as a grouse moor.

A number of blanket bogs were also searched. The first area checked was west of Stirling from Gillies Hill up to the wind farms on Craigengelt Hill north of Loch Coulter. No large heath were found here as many of the bogs had been drained, overgrazed or disturbed by development. In the area around the

Table 1. Showing the numbers of large heath butterflies seen when walking a 45 min transect at different sites. The numbers of transects carried out at each location and the historic numbers previously recorded there are also shown.

Site	Grid reference	Number in 45 min	Number transects	Historic records. Numbers – (date)
Shirgarton Moss (Near Kippen)	NS 646 962	867	1	98- (2005)
Killorn Moss (Near Arnprior)	NS 621 961	194	1	52-(2005)
East Moss Side (Near Thornhill)	NS 646 991	Range 10-127	2	7-(1905);2-(2001);7-(2005);6-(2006)
Poldar Moss (Near Thornhill)	NS 648 979	19	1	5-(1987); 1-(2005);1-(2008);10-(2010);10-(2011)
Easter Poldar Moss (South Flanders Moss)	NS 637 972	77	1	1-(2001);17-(2005)
Ballangrew Moss (Nr Port of Mentieth)	NS 621 981	96	1	17-(2005);7-(2007);2-(2006)
Central Flanders Moss	NS 634 983	range 0-80	18	2-(2001);1-(2012);5-(2006);1-(2007)
South Flanders Moss	NS 628 973	151	1	5-(1998)
Ochtertyre Moss (Nr Blairdrummond)	NS 734 974	0	1	1-(1905);0 – (2005)
Collymoon Moss (Nr Arnprior)	NS 587 966	47	1	N/A
Whitehill Moss (Nr Arnprior)	NS 587 972	19	1	N/A
Offerance Moss (Nr Gartmorn)	NS 537 957	82	1	36-(2005);5-(2007);5-(2009);15-(2010)
Wester Moss (Nr Fallin)	NS 836 908	23	1	65-(2003);19-(2004); 5-(2008); 21-(2010);10-(2011);3-(2012)
Dunmore and Easter Moss (Nr Cowie)	NS 867 891	0	14	N/A
Letham Moss (Nr Airth)	NS 881 860	0	1	Previous stronghold – (1979)
Slamannan Plateau (South of Falkirk)	NS 880 755	0	33	N/A
Fannyside lochs (SE Cumbernauld)	NS 803 739	0	24	N/A
Caldercruix	NS 815 694	0	12	1-(1980)
Blackridge	NS 906 670	0	22	N/A
Craigengelt Hill Area (West of Stirling)	NS 728 877	0	14	N/A
Achray Forest (North of Aberfoyle)	NN 515 028	0	3	N/A
Loch Rusky Area (South of Callander)	NN 615 030	0	11	1-(1979)
Brucefield Moss (East of Clackmannan)	NS 960 913	0	1	N/A
Dumyat Mosses	NS 817 983	0	6	2-(2010);3-(2011)
Braeleny (NE Callander)	NN 650 102	0	7	1-(1860)
Doune Wind Farm	NN 714 077	range 0-1	23	1-(1980)

Cocksburn reservoir on the Ochils east of Bridge of Allan had recent records and although remnants of this peatland still exist most was converted to wet grassland and none of the food plants were abundant enough. The north side of Dumyat has three peat bogs one of which (NS 833 981) is partly grazed and with little heather. Manchester treble bar and northern eggar moths were found but no large heath were discovered in spite of intensive surveys.

A population of large heath had previously been recorded at a site near Braeleny north east of Callander however it was not re-found. This was probably because these bogs had been heavily grazed and drained. Similarly surveys of the bogs surrounding the wind farm north of Doune also proved unproductive though a colony was reported there 36 years ago. Large areas of this blanket bog have been converted to forestry and a lot of drainage has been put in to the east of the wind farms. A volunteer Steven Wilkinson surveyed an area north of Cromlix where there are miles of hare's-foot cotton-grass and where he had previously seen large heath. Although he was unable to re-find the population he reported a new record (NN 7433-0944) north of The Bows and not far from Doune wind farm.

In conclusion we found that healthy colonies of large heath butterflies were almost entirely restricted to raised bogs particularly around the periphery of both the remains of Western Flanders Moss and Flanders Moss NNR. Wester Moss near Fallin is the only real exception. Many of these sites had been managed to block drainage ditches and remove tree growth either manually or by grazing. Collymoon and Whitehill Mosses were exceptions to this rule. Locations that had lost their large heath populations because of peat extraction and were recovering were not recolonised perhaps because the adult butterflies are so sedentary or that they are suseptible to winter flooding. We found that sites with reduced heather height and abundance appeared to have the highest numbers of large heath. The drainage of bogs produces conditions which frequently result in the loss of the butterfly's food plants which are crowded out as heather becomes dominant. As the bog continues to dry other woody shrubs and trees such as silver birch and Scot's pine establish acting to further desiccate and degrade the peatland. Although rewetting bogs by damming drainage ditches reduces the amount of heather, mature plants can survive so cutting or grazing the taller heather may help decrease its dominance.

Purple Hairstreak

The purple hairstreak *Favonius quercus* is a stunning but reclusive butterfly which flies from mid-July to early September. It has deep purple and black upperwings (Plate 11b) and is pale grey underneath with an orange eye spot. A relatively small insect (wingspan: 37-39 mm) it spends the entirety of its life in the canopy of oak trees, with a preference for the pedunculate oak *Quercus robur* (Futter et al. 2006). This butterfly is unusual as it depends on oak not only as a sole food plant for the caterpillars but is also the main sustenance for the adults. The butterflies do not nectar on flowers but instead sustain themselves on the honeydew of aphids. They rarely wander far from oaks though they have sometimes been observed flying to nearby sycamore and ash trees to feed on honeydew there. This species has long been considered under recorded because it is difficult to observe in the canopy (Thompson, 1978). The female is the most active of the sexes and is more frequently seen as they roam in the search for suitable trees to lay their eggs. The wings of the male butterfly differ from the females in that all upper-wings are largely purple (instead of mostly black) with a thin black border.

The purple hairstreak is widely thought to have suffered range contractions since Thompson's (1978) review however it is difficult to judge because of serious under-recording. In an attempt to clarify the local situation we surveyed the oak rich areas in the Forth Valley. They are most active in sunny weather when individuals can be seen chasing each other around the canopy particularly on warm sunny evenings. Mature trees were surveyed for a period of 20 minutes using both the naked eye and binoculars from 1st-31st August 2013. The pale underside of the butterfly can provide a bright contrast to the foliage and binoculars were often not required. Purple hairstreak's dependence on oak may suggest that they are quite sedentary, however we observed individuals flying across large bodies of water so they may disperse some distance to where oak trees are present.

Purple hairstreaks have been thought to be on the edge of their range in the Forth Valley area. Strong populations were known on the east side of Loch Lomond (in Stirlingshire) and in many of the oak woods from Drymen to Milngavie (Futter et al. 2006). To the east of these the only records were around Falkirk and Plean Country Park where we were able to confirm its presence in an area adjacent to Torwood. A growing number of casual observations in the Stirling area during the last few years seemed to indicate that they may be more common in the Forth Valley than previously thought.

Our survey confirmed the purple hairstreak could be found widely from Dollar to Loch Lomond side (Table 2). At Stirling University Campus the butterfly was seen in many of the large mature oak trees including those that form chains stretching to Logie Kirk where more sightings were made. To the east of the campus the next main area of oak trees is in Alva Glen where the butterfly was found. Stretching from Alva Glen to Dollar Glen there is a chain of oak woodland in field margins north of Tillicoultry and purple hairstreaks were recorded in all of these. The butterfly has been recorded recently in Dollar Glen and we confirmed the presence of reasonable numbers in the mature oaks which make up high proportion of the glen's trees. The paths that go up the glen sides give good observation points over the tree canopies and allow the butterfly to be easily seen. To the north west of Stirling University are Mine Woods in Bridge of Allan, however a number of surveys in good conditions failed to find the butterfly in the mature oaks there. Purple hairstreaks were found in the oaks along the Darn Walk between Bridge of Allan and Dunblane where the butterfly was observed making long flights across the river Allan appearing to go to ash trees to feed. From the valley of the Allan the oak woods extend up the Wharry Burn to the west where the species was found on both sides of Kippenrait Glen. Good viewing sites were found on the east edge of Dunblane golf course where it is possible to look over the canopies of mature oaks. The butterfly was found throughout Kippenrait Glen up to just north of Badgergate where the woodland becomes dominated by hazel.

Table 2. Records of Purple Hairstreak Surveys (N/S not surveyed, N/A no previous records)

Site name	**Grid reference**	**Numbers seen**	**Previous records. number-(date)**
Plean Country Park	NS 836 863	3	1-(1997)
Stirling University Grounds	NS 809 964	14	1-(2006)
Logie Kirk	NS 819 966	1	N/A
Alva Glen	NS 886 975	2	N/A
Tillicoultry	NS 928 980	2	N/A
Dollar Glen	NS 962 988	4	4-(2006)
Darn Walk, Bridge of Allan	NS 789 986	6	1-(2003)
Kippenrait Glen, Bridge of Allan	NS 797 996	7	N/A
Sheriffmuir, NE Gathering Stone	NN 806 026	14	N/A
A9 Bridge, Dunblane	NN 782 009	5	1-(1905)
Doune Castle	NN730 013	2	1-(1860)
Lanrick Woods, East of Buchany	NN 693 032	N/S	6-(2010)
Bracklinn Falls, Callander	NN 645 083	6	1-(1877)
Falls of Leny, Callander	NN 593 089	2	8-(2007)
Kilmahog , North Callander	NN 606 082	1	5-(2010)
River Teith, South of Callander	NN 653 048	N/S	1-(1905); 6-(1996)
Callander Craigs	NN 627 085	2	1-(1905)
South end of Loch Lubnaig	NN 587 092	16	N/A
South side Loch Venachar	NN576 050	9	N/A
Little Drum Wood, Brig o' Turk	NN 547 061	32	10-(2007);24-(2009);19-(2010); 4-(2012)
Landrick Lodge E of Brig o' Turk	NN 547 066	1	4-(2012)
South end of Glen Finglas	NN 531 074	5	4-(2012)
South end of Loch Katrine	NN 495 075	1	2-(2012)
Marshall Lodge, Aberfoyle	NN 523 014	6	3-(2012)
North of Gartmore	NS 529 987	2	1-(1905)
Loch Ard	NN 464 015	N/S	5-(2009);6-(2010);1-(1905)

Purple hairstreaks that can be seen in most of the oak trees around Dunblane golf course and downstream of the A9 bridge over the river Allan. Between Dunblane and Sheriffmuir there is an avenue of oak trees (NN 809 017) but the butterfly was not found in these. However on Sheriffmur NE of the Gathering Stone there is a copse of mature oak woodland (NN 804 027) with large numbers. The spacing of these trees brings their canopies down to a convenient viewing level and we were able to observe a lot of activity even on an overcast day. This footpath leading from the monument across the heather moor hosts spectacular numbers of vanessid butterflies (peacock, red admiral, painted lady and small tortoiseshell) in late August which nectar on the thousands of devil's bit scabious and knapweed plants by the side of the dry stone dyke. This was one of the first places locally where the comma butterfly was found and it also supports very high green hairstreak numbers in spring.

Butterfly Conservation records show the purple hairstreaks in several oak stances between Doune and Callander. The oaks around Doune Castle had the butterfly and in Callander itself we were able to confirm an old record at Bracklinn Falls. The new bridge provides an excellent viewing platform and allows close views of the butterfly in the oak canopy beneath. It is also still found in the woodland between Bracklinn Falls and Callander Craigs. The Craigs themselves have several historical records which we were able to confirm; again this site offers excellent views over oaks that grow partway up the slope.

Along the banks of the River Teith north of Callander the butterfly can be found in the woodlands near Kilmahog (NN 600 088) and Falls of Leny (NN 593 089). The metal bridge at the south end of Loch Lubnaig (NN 593 089) is raised to the level of the oak canopies on the bank either side and provided some of the best views of the butterfly in the survey. Again butterflies were observed crossing the river and visiting ash trees. Purple hairstreaks were not found north of this point though oak woods were surveyed; along the west shore of Loch Lubnaig; beside the A84 up to Lochearnhead; along the south shore of Loch Earn. To the south east of Callander there were a number of oak stands as well as previous Butterfly Conservation records near Loch Rusky, though this area was not resurveyed.

West of Callander we found purple hairstreak along the length of the south bank of Loch Venachar. On the north bank at the west end of the loch we found good numbers in the Woodland Trust's Little Drum Wood. This oak woodland contains many low growing trees along the ascending sections of the footpath to Brig o' Turk and provides exceptionally good viewing points in sunny weather. Unsurprisingly this site holds the largest number of reported records in the Forth Valley area. Further sightings were made directly across the A821 near Landrick Lodge and in the woodland that runs along the burn between Brig o' Turk village and the dam at the end of Glen Finglas reservoir. It was also found close by in the oak woods at the south end of Loch Katrine where the butterfly had been previously recorded.

To the south in the Trossachs purple hairstreaks had been found in a number of oaks around the David Marshal Lodge and the coppiced oak walk provides regular sightings in the flight period. South of Aberfoyle outside the village of Gartmore (NS 530 987) we also confirmed old records. From this population there is a chain of established purple hairstreak sites running south from Drymen down to Mugdock Country Park near Milngavie (Futter et al. 2006) where we confirmed the butterflies presence.

We also surveyed along the West Highland Way on the east side of Loch Lomond to find the butterfly's northern limit. On the banks of Loch Lomond purple hairstreaks were found from Balmaha at regular intervals to just south of Rowardennan. A good area to view it is at Sallochy (NS 391 946) where there is a steep rise in the land beside the loch with a bank of oak trees hosting large numbers. North of Sallochy no sightings were made until Inversnaid. These observations confirm Butterfly Conservation records showing the butterfly is present in most oak woods from Milngavie to Inversnaid which seems to be its northern limit. Just north of Inversnaid the woodland becomes dominated by alder and there is a significant gap before reaching a small patch of oak in Glen Falloch at Inveranan (NN 320 180) where no purple hairstreaks were found.

It is clear from our report that purple hairstreaks are far more widespread than previous records indicate and hopefully the study will provide a baseline to assess the future health of the local population.

Northern Brown Argus

The northern brown argus *Aricia artaxerxes* (Plate 12a) is a nationally scarce UK BAP priority species. The butterfly's flight period is from mid-June until the end of July and its sole food plant is the common rock-rose *Helianthemum nummularium*. This plant favours sheltered, south facing slopes on base-rich soils which is a rare and localised habitat in Clackmannanshire largely confined to the steep scarp slopes above Menstrie and Alva. Previous records of the butterfly in the Forth Valley area are restricted to small isolated populations located in the Ochils. Thomson (1976) found a historic record for the species on Dumyat in 1845 and it was described as 'not uncommon' in the hills around Menstrie and Logie in 1852. He discusses how between 1860 and 1900 the Scotch Brown Argus, as it was called then, had disappeared from its locations in Central Scotland. Although Thomson (1976) does not mention its presence in Alva Glen it is a well known historic site and there are also recent records close by on Craigleith SSSI (Gallacher, 2007). In 2004 John Gallacher (2007) carried out surveys of both the butterfly and its food plant and confirmed the former's presence at these two locations. Gallacher stresses the precarious nature of these Hillfoot populations and particularly the adverse effect of gorse encroachment and the over grazing of the food plant.

In our surveys (1st July-7th August 2103) we found that the most effective method was not to depend on observing the butterflies but rather to search for the presence of the eggs which are distinctively laid on the upper surface of common rock-rose leaves (Plate 12b). We resurveyed the areas covered by Gallacher (2007) and found many of the sites had changed dramatically since 2004.

Gallacher had been concerned how the prime site of Northern Brown Argus in Alva Glen (NS 884 980) had been fenced to exclude sheep to aid woodland regeneration. He feared that this would prove detrimental to the butterfly's grassland habitat and result in its decline. Unfortunately his predictions proved correct as the common rock-rose had been reduced by encroaching vegetation which would have otherwise been controlled by sheep. It is unclear to what extent this has had an impact on the Alva Glen butterfly population since recorders have used inconsistent surveying methods. Another site surveyed by Gallacher was Wee Torrie Hill (NS 880 978) where he found a strong population of northern brown argus. He also mentioned that the surrounding gorse in this area was managed through gorse burning and when we found this rock-rose colony it had subsequently been destroyed by an extensive fire. Sadly this would have taken this butterfly population with it.

Thankfully not all sites have suffered such devastating losses. Craig Leith (NS 874 977) 0.5 km to the west of Alva Glen proved to be significantly better than when last surveyed in 2004 with high numbers of eggs present on thousands of rock-rose plants. These impressive numbers were present on a section of the craig which was steep enough to prevent sheep from grazing the food plant but allowed them to keep encroaching scrub in check. The steepness of the slopes also prevented our access to most of the rock-rose plants but if the egg numbers were similar throughout this colony it is likely to be a very important site for the butterfly. We also found a new site for the species on the west side of Myreton Hill (NS 854 978) where rock-rose plants possessed similar numbers of northern brown argus eggs to those in Alva Glen. The impact of sheep grazing was seen at a second site where a rock-rose colony recorded in early June was virtually eliminated by the time of the survey. Gallacher (2007) reported that he could not locate any butterfly populations at the sites of historical records on The Kipps below Dumyat (NS 839 973). We resurveyed these cliffs (using binoculars) and can confirm that only four small patches of rock-rose survive. Older articles also refer to the top of Dumyat as a stronghold of the butterfly, however we found only six small non-flowering patches of rock-rose in a nearby valley (NS 827 973) and these had no northern brown argus eggs on them.

Many of the sites which could of supported northern brown argus have been subjected to inappropriate grazing levels and gorse encroachment. All sites where the butterfly persisted were on slopes where the rock-rose plants were only susceptible to light or no grazing pressure. Previous studies found the butterfly's preferred habitat was low, uneven sward heights (6-10 cm), which provide shelter for the adults and warmer microclimates for the development of the caterpillars. Correct management of the food plant sites to provide these conditions is essential if the future of this spectacular little butterfly is to be safeguarded.

References

Asher, J. Warren, M. Fox, R. Harding, P. Jeffcoate, G. and Jeffcoate, S. 2001. The Millennium Atlas of Butterflies in Britain and Ireland. Oxford: Oxford University Press.

Futter, K. Sutcliffe, R. Welham, D. Welham, A. Rostron, A.J. MacKay, J. Gregory, N. McCleary, J. Tait, T.N. Black, J. Kirkland, P. 2006. Butterflies of South West Scotland. Glendaruel: Argyll Publishing.

Gallacher, J. 2007. The Northern Brown Argus in the Ochil hills Clackmannanshire. *Forth Naturalist and Historian.* **30**, 73-80.

Ordnance Survey. (2014). Using: EDINA Digimap Ordnance Survey Service, http://digimap.edina.ac.uk.Downloaded: July 29, 2014.Crown Copy Right 2014.

Pickett, D. and Stoneman, J. 2005. Surveying the Large Heath Butterfly with Volunteers in Stirlingshire. Forth Naturalist and Historian. **28**, 13-20.

Thomson, G. 1976. Our Disappearing Butterflies. *Forth Naturalist and Historian.* **1**, 89-103.